Oceanography and Our Future

Learning Trends

A DIVISION OF GLOBE BOOK COMPANY, INC.

NEW YORK · CHICAGO · DALLAS

Oceanography and Our Future

Joseph M. Oxenhorn
Burton I. Goldfeld

SENIOR AUTHOR: JOSEPH M. OXENHORN

has taught the sciences in various secondary schools and has served as principal of elementary, junior, and senior high schools. He has been active in science syllabus construction and has trained science teachers. Since his retirement from his post as Principal of Theodore Roosevelt High School, he has served as Director of Science and Senior Science Author for Globe Book Co. He is the author of the *Pathways in Science Series, Pathways in Biology,* and a textbook for teachers on methods of teaching science.

ASSOCIATE AUTHOR: BURTON I. GOLDFELD

started his career in the secondary schools of England. In the last ten years, he has served as Instructor in Oceanography and Biology at North High School in Valley Stream, New York. He serves as Instructor in Environmental Science at the North Shore Junior Science Museum in Port Washington, New York. He is also an accomplished scuba diver and a marine naturalist.

CONSULTANTS

Maxwell Cohen, Chairman, Department of Science and Oceanography, Beach Channel High School, New York, N.Y.

J. Darrell Barnard, Professor Emeritus, Science Education, New York University, Associate Director of COPES, N.Y.U.

The authors are indebted to Mrs. Ruth G. Oxenhorn of the Plainview, New York, school system for her assistance.

Editorial, art and production assistance provided by Center for Media Development, Inc.

ISBN: 0–87065–715–1

PRINTED IN THE UNITED STATES OF AMERICA

0 9 8 7 6 5 4 3 2

Contents

Introduction

Welcome to your new science book, OCEANOGRAPHY AND OUR FUTURE.

Science as applied to our environment is a most important field. Your knowledge in this field will help you to be a well-informed citizen. It may even help you in your life's work.

This book is a tool for learning. A good mechanic knows how to use tools. A good student knows how to use a book.

ARRANGEMENT

At the front of the book is a *Table of Contents*. This table or list tells you what you can find in the book. It tells you on what page each part of the book can be found.

The book is divided into four parts called *Units*.

Each unit is divided into *Chapters*. Each chapter begins with a *Problem* which is answered by material in that chapter. For example, you will find Chapter 1 on page 2. The *problem question* there is: What is the science of the oceans?

Each chapter is divided into SECTIONS which have hyphenated numbers. Turn to page 19. There you will find Section 3–2, *Early Diving Methods*. Section 3–3 is titled *Breathing Under Water*. The first number in each case is the chapter number. The second number is the section in that chapter.

Every few *Section*s you will find a section called *Learned So Far*. Turn to page 22 for an example. This is a kind of summary of what you just read. It helps you review. It helps you remember.

At the end of each chapter, you will find questions that test how much you have learned. Turn to page 26. There you will find the section called *Knowing and Understanding*. In addition to the questions, you will also find suggestions for exciting things you can do at home. Look at page 87, Question V.

NEW SCIENCE WORDS

Science has its own language. It has new words which have a special meaning. Some of these words are not familiar. The book tells you how to pronounce these words. Turn to page 2. We use the word *NAVIGATORS*. Notice how it is pronounced: NAV is in capitals. This is the part of the word that is stressed (accented).

GLOSSARY *(Oceanography Dictionary)*

At the end of the book, page 176, there is a *Glossary*. This is a short "dictionary" for the book. It is arranged in alphabetical order.

INDEX

Beginning on page 180, there is an alphabetical index to help you look up information.

PICTURES, DIAGRAMS, AND CHARTS

The book has many pictures and diagrams to help you "see" science ideas. All pictures and diagrams are numbered in such a way that you can find them quickly. For example, Figure 19–1 means the first picture on page 19. Figure 25–2 means the second picture on page 25. Most illustrations have a caption which explains what you are looking at. Often, there are also questions to help you learn more about the illustration.

INVESTIGATIONS

Your book has many investigations. Some of them will be done by your teacher in class. Some you will do in class by yourself or with a partner. Some you can do at home. Investigations are activities that give a scientist answers. They are great fun and a good way to learn.

UNIT I

Oceans of the World

WHAT'S IT ALL ABOUT?

Seventy-one percent of our earth—almost three-quarters—is covered by water. No wonder our oceans have been the subject of so much study and interest!

Scientists are pretty sure that all life began in the sea. Early man wondered at the nature of the sea. The roar of the ocean, the power of crashing waves, and vast sights "without end" made for mystery and fear. In early times, the sea was man's "highway," and much of our early history was made on or near it.

Man's first trips to the sea were made close to shore in small, crude ships. Mostly he searched for fish, which were precious food. Later, he developed larger boats and took to the seas for adventure. His explorations brought him to new lands—lands of strange people, unheard-of plants and animals, precious metals, and gems. His travels also changed his whole idea of geography.

But it was not all adventure and romance. The hardships of the seas brought death and destruction. Also, mighty warships were used in bloody sea battles in long wars among nations.

Now there is a new day in history. Our explorations are made not only *on* the ocean but also *in* the ocean—deep down and on the bottom. It is no longer enough to know how to handle a ship. It is a complicated business of science and engineering; of experiments and tests and data. Nations are still rivals, but their search in the oceans is now friendly and cooperative.

And so we turn to the science of *OCEANOGRAPHY*. In our first *Unit*, we shall meet the ocean scientists, hear about their problems, and learn about the tools of their trade.

CHAPTER 1

Studying the Oceans Around Us

PROBLEM:
*What is the science
of the oceans?*

1-1 THE LOST ATLANTIS

The stories of the early Greek writers tell us that a great island was once located in the Atlantic. The island, which was called *ATLANTIS* (at-LAN-tus), was inhabited by a very strong and proud people who wished to conquer all of Europe. The Greeks were supposed to have saved the Europeans from the invading armies of this ocean kingdom. For its wickedness, the island was struck by an earthquake which lasted a day and a night. The island disappeared into the sea—never to be seen again.

Is this just a tale? Is there really a lost city lying somewhere in the Atlantic? We may never know. But this story does serve to point out our early interest in the sea. Today more than ever, the seas and oceans are being studied and talked about. Let's find out . . .

1-2 WHO STUDIES THE OCEANS?

A lot of people have been studying the oceans for a great many years. There are *NAVIGATORS* (NAV-uh-gay-turz) who are concerned with ocean travel. There are map makers, direction

FIG. 3–1. Atlantis, the "lost island" of an ancient legend.

finders, and place locators. There are *GEOGRAPHERS* (jee-OG-ruh-furz). More recently, there are the new scientists, the *OCEANOGRAPHERS* (o-shu-NOG-ruh-furz).

1–3 THE SCIENCE OF OCEANOGRAPHY

What is oceanography the study of? The answer is: anything and everything about oceans. To give you a better idea of what this means, let's look into the work of some of the early oceanographers.

Matthew Fontaine *MAURY* (MAW-ree), an American naval officer, is known as the "Father of Oceanography." He was most interested in the *PHYSICS* (FIZ-iks) of the sea. He studied currents, depths, climates, and temperatures for many years. From his observations, he developed charts of winds and currents month by month. Later in his life, he published the first real textbook about oceanography.

Edward *FORBES* was a Scotsman who studied living things found in the sea. His interest was in *BIOLOGY* (by-OL-uh-jee). He investigated how far down in the sea life could exist.

FIG. 3–2. Maury (1806–1873) and Forbes (1815–1854). What problems do you think they faced?

3

The oceans have been called the "largest water solution in the world." Many chemicals, both elements and compounds, are dissolved in the oceans. (See Figure 81–1, page 81.) Oceanographers must therefore study the *CHEMISTRY* (KEM-is-tree), or composition, of ocean water.

The oceans are also really a part of the earth—the water over the crust of the earth. Therefore, oceanographers study rocks and rock movements. That part of their study is called *GEOLOGY* (jee-OL-uh-jee).

Fig. 4–1.

1–4 THE GREAT VOYAGE

December 21, 1872, was a cold, rainy day. The 2,300-ton ship was ready to set out from England. What a strange ship! It had chart rooms, microscopes, bottles, tanks, and nets. The 223 crew members and scientists stood at attention on the deck as the ship slipped away. It was the research ship *CHALLENGER*—the greatest ocean-studying vessel of its time.

It sailed around the world's oceans for 3½ years. Scientists aboard collected all sorts of information. They drew maps of the ocean bottom. They took bottom-of-ocean temperatures. They located the exact positions of many islands and rocks. Many new animal groups were discovered. The results of these studies were published in 50 large books.

As we shall see later, today's ocean research ships are very complicated floating laboratories.

FIG. 5–1.
The *Challenger* traveled the world's oceans collecting information about the sea.

LEARNED SO FAR

● Oceanography is a combination science of the physics, chemistry, geology, and biology of the oceans.
● Maury and Forbes were early oceanographers.
● The *Challenger* was a nineteenth-century ocean research ship.

1–5 THE EARTH AND ITS WATERS

The outer surface, or *CRUST*, of the earth is made of rock. The *CONTINENTS* lie on *GRANITE* (GRAN-it). Granite is rock formed millions of years ago by the slow cooling of liquid minerals. The oceans lie on *BASALT* (buh-SALT). Basalt is rock formed when the *LAVA* (LAH-vuh) of ancient volcanoes cooled rapidly.

Almost three-quarters of the earth's surface (71 percent) is covered by water. This part of the earth is called the *HYDROSPHERE* (HY-druh-sfeer). The hydrosphere is really one big ocean. Sticking up out of the water are the various large masses called *CONTINENTS* and smaller masses called *ISLANDS*. For purposes of geography, we call different parts of the ocean by separate names. There are 4 oceans and 21 seas. Some geographers now speak of one ocean: *The World Ocean.*

Examine Fig. 6–1 below. This shows how the waters of the earth are distributed. You can now understand why we refer to a "water hemisphere" and to a "land hemisphere."

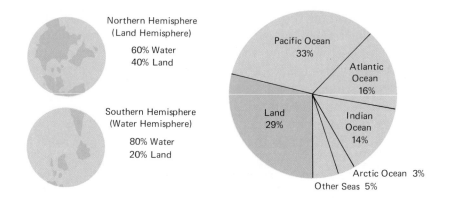

FIG. 6–1. Where is most of the land? Where is most of the water? Add the percentage of water in the three smallest oceans. How does this compare with the Pacific Ocean?

1–6   WHERE DID THE WATERS COME FROM?

Let's imagine we have a special time machine that can take us back billions of years to the earth's beginning. We set the dials of our time machine for 4½ billion years. Away we go!

What does it look like? Everywhere we see hot rocks with huge open cracks. These cracks lead to active volcanoes. We see *vapor* (steam) oozing out of the cracks. The vapor escapes into the atmosphere to form clouds.

If we returned a billion years later, we would find that the earth had begun to cool and had formed huge amounts of liquid water from the clouds. This is the process of *CONDENSATION* (kon-den-SAY-shun). The waters began to collect in the ridges and valleys to form the early oceans.

There was a time when the water kept changing to vapor as it touched the hot rocks. Then it condensed again. When the rocks finally cooled, the *great ocean basin* was formed.

Why doesn't the water leave the oceans now? Or does it? Follow the water cycle in Figure 7–1 below. Its scientific name is the *HYDROLOGIC* (hy-druh-LOJ-ik) cycle. Start with the ocean.

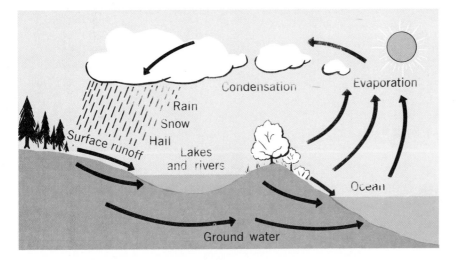

Fig. 7–1. The hydrologic cycle. What happens to rain, snow, and hail? Does the water from rivers and streams always enter the ocean immediately? Explain your answer.

1–7 OCEANOGRAPHY AND YOU

So you don't live near the ocean. And you think it doesn't matter to you. Wrong! Whether we live on prairies, in mountains, or on deserts, the ocean affects us all.

The oceans are part of our environment. They have a great influence on our weather and climate. They give us a means of transportation. They provide food. Eighty-five percent of the world's oxygen is produced in the oceans. They are rich in minerals and oil. They are a source of great wealth for the future of humanity.

Is there a future for you in oceanography? With the sudden burst of interest in oceanography, many people will find new careers. Some will become oceanographers as scientists. Some will be skilled workers on ships. Some will work in shore plants or laboratories. Are you interested in a career of this type? Learn as much science as you can.

OCEANS OF THE WORLD

Ocean	Millions of Square Miles	Width	Average Depth
Pacific	64	10,000 mi.	14,000 ft.
Atlantic	32	3,600 mi.	12,800 ft.
Indian	28	6,000 mi.	13,000 ft.
Arctic	5	3,000 mi.	4,000 ft.

LEARNED SO FAR

● The waters of the earth form the hydrosphere.
● The surface of the earth is covered with oceans surrounding continents and other land forms.
● Oceanography is a new field which will provide job opportunities for men and women in the future.

Self-Study Guide for Chapter 1

I. KNOWING AND UNDERSTANDING. FIND THE ANSWER. WRITE IT IN YOUR NOTEBOOK.

1. The tale of the lost city of Atlantis reminds us that
   a. civilization had an early interest in the sea.
   b. earthquakes destroyed it.
   c. Greeks were very strong.
   d. the city was destroyed in a day and night.
2. Maury's interest in the ocean centered around
   a. the life of the sea.
   b. the composition of ocean water.
   c. the currents and depths.
   d. the rocks of the sea.
3. To understand the types of materials on the sea bottom, an oceanographer should know about
   a. the field of geology.
   b. the temperature of the water.
   c. the color of the water.
   d. the climate in the area.

4. Which of the following can help us explore for oil under the oceans?
   a. A navigator.
   b. A geographer.
   c. A marine biologist.
   d. All three.

II. FIND THE EXPLANATION. IN WHICH SECTION OF THE CHAPTER IS THE ANSWER TO EACH OF THE FOLLOWING QUESTIONS? WRITE THE QUESTION AND THE ANSWER IN YOUR NOTEBOOK.

1. What investigations did the *Challenger* make?
2. What sciences should the oceanographer be familiar with?
3. What is a geologist?
4. Which hemisphere has the most ocean water?

III. TRUE OR FALSE? IF THE STATEMENT IS TRUE, WRITE *TRUE*. IF THE STATEMENT IS FALSE, GIVE A WORD TO BE USED INSTEAD OF THE *CAPITALIZED* WORD, SO THAT THE STATEMENT WILL BE TRUE.

1. Matthew Maury was interested in the BIOLOGY of the sea.
2. The *ATLANTIS* made a famous oceanographic voyage.
3. The study of the oceans is known as OCEANOGRAPHY.
4. The HYDROSPHERE forms seas, bays, and oceans.

IV. IN AN ENCYCLOPEDIA, LOOK UP THE VOYAGE OF THE *H.M.S. CHALLENGER*. WRITE A REPORT OF YOUR FINDINGS. USE THE FOLLOWING GUIDELINES:

1. Dates.
2. Route.
3. Instruments.
4. Findings (discoveries).

CHAPTER 2

Tools of the Oceanographer

PROBLEM:
*How do we study
the science of
oceanography?*

2–1   HOW DO WE STUDY OCEANOGRAPHY?

Oceanography is a *science*. As in other sciences, the most important method of learning is by *observation*. Observation means careful *watching*. Observation uses all senses, not only sight. For example, an oceanographer *listens* to echoes in the ocean. He may *smell* a sample of water. He *feels* the rocks, the seaweed, and the sea animals with his fingers.

FIG. 10–1. How are these students using their powers of observation in learning about oceans?

As the oceanographer makes his observations or collects *DATA* (DAY-tuh), he keeps careful notes. From his observations, he develops a "hunch" or *HYPOTHESIS* (hy-POTH-uh-sis) as a temporary explanation. As he gathers more facts, his hypothesis may become a *THEORY* (THEE-uh-ree), which is a stronger explanation.

Like other scientists, the oceanographer performs investigations or *EXPERIMENTS* (ex-PER-uh-ments) to test the truth or error of his hypothesis or theory. Some theories hold up and are accepted; others are found to be wrong and are thrown out.

2–2 WHERE DO WE STUDY OCEANOGRAPHY?

Your first answer might be, "In or on the oceans." A better answer is "Indoors, outdoors, everywhere."

The oceanographer travels to distant places to study special areas of the ocean. He goes below the surface of the oceans, sometimes to the very bottom. Often he works at the seashore.

Can you study oceanography indoors? Of course.

Indoors, the oceanographer studies his samples, arranges his data, and sets up his experiments. He works in a modern, well-equipped *LABORATORY* (LAB-ruh-tor-ee).

Like other scientists, the oceanographer is often in the *library*, reading about the data and the experiments of other oceanographers. Sometimes he meets with other oceanographers at *conventions* to discuss problems with his fellow scientists.

FIG. 11–1. What kinds of work are done in an oceanographic laboratory?

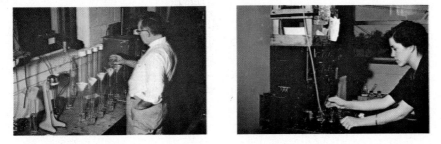

2–3 TAKING MEASUREMENTS IN OCEANOGRAPHY

Science is *precise*. The scientist cannot always trust his senses. He therefore uses instruments to get his measurements.

As a scientist, the oceanographer uses well-known instruments. For example, he uses *thermometers* to measure temperature. He uses *barometers* to measure pressure. He uses *tapes* and *rulers* to measure distances. He uses *scales* to measure the mass of objects (measured as weight).

The units of his measurements may be either English or metric. But in addition to the usual scientific instruments, oceanographers use very special equipment. We shall learn about it in the section that follows.

LEARNED SO FAR

- Oceanography, as a science, depends on observation to develop theories.
- Theories are tested by experiments.
- Oceanographers work outdoors (in the field) and indoors (labs, libraries, and conventions).
- Oceanographers use instruments for precise measurements.

2–4 LIMITS IN THE DEEP WATER

When you dive to the bottom of a pool, do you feel your ears get stuffy? This is because water pressure becomes greater, the deeper you go. There is a limit to how far down we can go into the sea. The limit for a diver using the *COMPRESSED* (kom-PREST) air unit for breathing is about 450 to 600 feet. Of course, divers have gone to greater depths in special chambers. One such dive took two men to a depth of 38,000 feet. In Chapter 3, we shall learn more about deep diving.

2–5 FLOATING LABORATORIES

To transport tools to the sea, the oceanographer uses well-equipped research vessels. These vessels are outfitted with laboratories for advanced work at sea. Usually, the ships are run by a university or government organization.

FIG. 13–1. The *Atlantis II* is a research vessel.

The *Atlantis II* is a vessel operated by the Woods Hole Laboratory in Massachusetts. It is 210 feet long and can carry 25 scientists and 28 crew members. The ship has a controlled-temperature aquarium, a fully equipped machine shop, and an underwater observation chamber. There are four large laboratories on board.

2–6   TRAPPING A WATER SAMPLE

In 1770, Benjamin Franklin made the first chart of the Gulf Stream. He measured the temperature of the water in the current and outside it. His equipment was a bucket and rope, which he dropped over the side of the ship. After the bucket was hauled aboard ship, he measured the water temperature.

Today, the oceanographer uses an instrument known as the *NANSEN BOTTLE* (NAN-sun). A special tube traps water at a certain depth and records its temperature. It is more accurate than the bucket and line, since the temperature of ocean water changes as you go deeper. Back on board ship, scientists perform further tests on the water. For example, they may check the amount of *OXYGEN* (OX-uh-jin) or test its salt content.

FIG. 13–2. This researcher is using a Nansen bottle. What advantage is there in using this instrument?

2–7 LIGHTING IT UP...

It has been said that the sea is a dark, silent world. This is true in the deeper parts of the ocean. But in the shallow coastal regions, light does go through. Marine biologists are interested in how far into the sea light can reach, since plants can grow only where there is light. The depth to which light can reach depends upon the clearness of the water. What makes one body of water clear and blue and the other green and cloudy? In Unit III, we will learn that *MICROSCOPIC* (my-kruh-SKOP-ik) plants and animals are found in seawater. When they are present in great numbers, the water can become green and cloudy. Light could not pass very far into such water.

A simple instrument to measure the clearness of water is the *SECCHI DISK* (SEK-ee). It is simply a round plate with a weight at its end. The plate is lowered into the sea until it disappears. The depth at which it first disappears is recorded.

2–8 LIGHT THROUGH SEAWATER

DO AND DISCOVER

PROBLEM: How can you measure the amount of light passing through water?

PROCEDURES

Using your Secchi disk, try measuring the passing of light in a bay, pond, or swimming pool.
1. Make a record of weather conditions. For example, note whether it was sunny, and whether the water was calm or rough.
2. Lower the disk into the water, using the rope.
3. Record the depth at which the disk disappears from sight.

OBSERVATIONS AND ANALYSIS
1. In what areas did you find the greatest light?
2. How could you increase the penetration?

FIG. 14–1. The Secchi disk. How is this used?

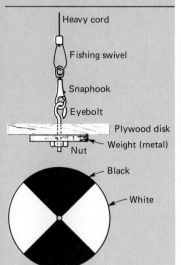

Construction of a simple Secchi Disk

(These materials may be found in any school shop, or they may be purchased for little cost.)

Materials:

Heavy cord
Fishing swivel
Snaphook, eyebolt and nut
Heavy weight with hole for eyebolt
Paint: Black enamel
      White enamel
      Marine varnish

Heavy cord
Fishing swivel
Snaphook
Eyebolt
Plywood disk
Weight (metal)
Nut
Black
White

1. Paint plywood black and white.
2. Cover with one or two coats of marine varnish.

● Oceanography is a science and uses observation and experimentation.
● Oceanographers must use instruments to make precise observations of the sea.
● To trap water samples, scientists use the Nansen bottles.
● Light penetration is measured with a Secchi disk.

2-9 A DEEP-SEA SAFARI

To collect animals and plants from the ocean's depths, oceanographers use *NETS* and *DREDGES* (DREJ-iz). A dredge is a special shovel used to scoop up material from river or sea bottoms. For microscopic animals and plants, they use a *PLANKTON NET* (PLANK-tun), a small cone-shaped net which is towed behind a boat.

To collect fish, the scientist uses the *MIDWATER TRAWL*. This is a large net which uses a weight to keep it at the right depth.

FIG. 15–1.
This is a plankton net used for collecting microscopic plants and animals. Can the net be used for other animals?

2-10 STORIES IN THE MUD

Strange as it may seem, a story may be told from a mud sample taken from the ocean floor. A sample from the sea may give the geologist a clue to the age of the earth. To obtain these samples, a *CORER* (KOR-ur) is used. It is simply a long tube which is pushed into the sea bottom. A small cylinder of mud is then trapped inside the tube. We shall learn more about the corer in a later chapter.

FIG. 15–2.
A corer is used to obtain samples from the sea floor. How can this help the scientist understand the earth?

15

2–11 PROBING THE DEPTHS

How deep is the ocean? This was one of the first questions asked by early scientists. They found ways of *sounding* the depths. It was a simple method called *line sounding*. (See EXERCISE VI, page 18, at the end of this chapter.) Today we use more accurate methods.

Place yourself in a dark room. Try to find your direction without turning on the light. Difficult? You said it! But a bat has no trouble with this. Bats give out high-pitched squeaks which humans cannot hear. The squeaks bounce off solid objects and back to the bat's very sensitive ears. In other words, the bat uses a type of direction finder.

The sea is a dark place also. Much of what we know about the great depths has come from the use of sound waves. The use of sound to measure the ocean bottom is called *ECHO SOUNDING* (EK-o). A sound is sent out from an instrument in the ship. Aboard ship, the scientist listens for its echo. The speed of sound waves through water is known to be about 5,000 feet per second. The time it takes for the echo to return from the sea floor helps to estimate depth. If it takes one second to hit bottom, it will take another second to return. (Two seconds = a depth of 5,000 feet.)

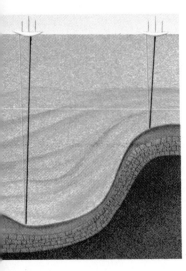

Fig. 16–1.
The use of sound to measure the ocean bottom is called echo sounding.

LEARNED SO FAR

- Microscopic animals and plants can be collected in special nets.
- Larger creatures are collected in trawls.
- A corer is used to take whole bottom samples.
- Sound waves are used to estimate the depths of the ocean.

Self-Study Guide for Chapter 2

I. KNOWING AND UNDERSTANDING. FIND THE ANSWER. WRITE
    IT IN YOUR NOTEBOOK.

    1. Benjamin Franklin's simple method of collecting water temper-
       atures was not accurate because
       a. he sent his bucket down too far.
       b. water temperatures change the deeper you go.
       c. he didn't use the correct thermometer.
       d. he didn't measure properly.
    2. The Nansen bottle can
       a. collect animals at a certain depth.
       b. collect microscopic plants and animals.
       c. trap a water sample and record its temperature.
       d. measure the oxygen content of a water sample.
    3. By using echo sounding, the oceanographer can estimate the
       depth of the ocean because
       a. he knows sound waves travel fast.
       b. the sound waves echo.
       c. he can determine the time it takes for the echo of the sound
          wave to bounce back.
       d. he can estimate the depth.
    4. Before an oceanographer can solve a problem, questions are
       asked which lead to
       a. a conclusion.
       b. a hypothesis.
       c. an answer.
       d. a control.

II. FIND THE EXPLANATION. IN WHICH SECTION OF THE CHAP-
    TER IS THE ANSWER TO EACH OF THE FOLLOWING QUES-
    TIONS? WRITE THE QUESTION AND THE ANSWER IN YOUR
    NOTEBOOK.

    a. How can our senses be used to study science?
    b. Why is it important to know the speed of sound waves when
       using the echo sounder?
    c. What could cause water to lose its clearness?
    d. Where is oceanography studied?

III. FINISH THE STORY. USE THE WORDS FROM THE LIST BELOW. WRITE THE STORY IN YOUR NOTEBOOK.

An oceanographic ship is traveling out to sea. The scientists plan to study the depth of the ocean. They will use (1) ————. To study water clearness they will make use of the (2) ————. The scientists plan to collect some microscopic life. They will use the (3) ————. Some scientists are interested in the age of the earth. They plan to take some (4) ————.

plankton net	core samples
echo sounding	Nansen bottle
dredges	research vessel
	Secchi disk

IV. PUT ON YOUR THINKING CAP!

1. What is one of today's biggest problems in studying oceanography? Why?
2. Why should every experiment be written up clearly?
3. How is scientific research like detective work?
4. Why is there so much talk about changing the United States's system of measurement to the metric system? Do you approve? Why?

V. WHICH IS THE OUTSIDER? ONE WORD DOES NOT BELONG WITH THE OTHER THREE. WRITE THE WORD.

1. Depth, echo, color, sound.
2. Color, light, clearness, core.
3. Net, trawl, dredge, Secchi disk.

VI. A PROJECT FOR THE OCEANOGRAPHY CLUB.

How deep is a lake, a swimming pool, a bay? You can find out. Use the *line sounding* method.
1. Take a long fishing line; make a knot every 6 feet. Tie a heavy lead weight (about 5 pounds) to one end.
2. Lower the weight slowly into the water. As the weight goes down, count the number of knots.
3. If you count 10 knots, your lake is (10 × 6) 60 feet deep. Six knots = (6 × 6) 36 feet.
4. Each 6 feet, knot to knot, is called a *fathom*.
This is the line sounding used by the *Challenger*. (Only they used a 200-pound weight!)

CHAPTER 3

Exploring the Deep

PROBLEM:
*How does man explore
under water?*

3–1   LOOKING BACK...

If you've ever tried diving, you know that you can stay under water for less than a minute. Some professional divers are able to last for a little over two minutes. The record for a *breath-holding* dive is 217½ feet in 40 seconds. How, then, can a person stay under water for longer lengths of time?

The first way was with the "old-fashioned" diving suits. Later, breathing devices or "underwater lungs" were developed. The most modern way is the *underwater research vehicle* or U.R.V.

3–2   EARLY DIVING METHODS

Early diving equipment used the diving suit, heavy helmet, and heavy weights. Compressed air was fed to the helmet through a long coiled tube. The diver could communicate to the surface through a telephone.

3–3   BREATHING UNDER WATER

History books tell us that man's first venture under water for long periods of time was using air bags made of animal skins. These bags were taken to the bottom by divers. When the air

FIG. 19–1.
How does the diving suit overcome three problems—water pressure, cold, and oxygen—in going below the ocean surface? What problems still exist?

Fig. 20–1. Divers can explore under water with the aid of an aqualung or scuba. But are there still problems, even with the scuba?

was used up, men on board ships lowered down new bags. It was not until 1943, however, that Jacques Yves Cousteau and Emile Gagnon developed the *AQUALUNG* or *SCUBA* (SKOO-buh; *S*elf-*C*ontained *U*nderwater *B*reathing *A*pparatus). With the scuba, a diver could swim under water without a connection to the surface. He could stay submerged for an hour or more, depending upon the air supply in his tanks.

In the scuba, tanks of compressed air are strapped to the diver's back. The high-pressure air from the tanks is changed to regular breathing pressure by a special automatic regulator attached to the tank. Scuba divers are called "free divers" since they are not anchored by tubes and lines. Today a diver can reach an average depth of about 135 feet. Scuba is a new tool of science. It is also a new sport.

3–4 THE "WELL-DRESSED" DIVER

A well-dressed diver wears a face mask and swim fins. Where the water is extremely cold, a special diving suit is worn.

The face mask covers the nose as well as the eyes. It provides an air space between the eyes and the water. This permits the diver to see clearly under water. Flippers or swim fins help the diver to move easily through the water. Only the diver's feet are then required for swimming, leaving the diver's hands free to do other work.

Along with these developments came the *dry suit* and the *wet suit*. These inventions protect the diver against cold water. *Dry suits* keep the water away from the body. The rubber of the suit forms an airtight seal over the diver's body. Woolen underwear beneath the suit gives extra warmth. The *wet suit* is made of foam rubber. Tiny air bubbles in the rubber provide insulation. A little bit of water is allowed to seep in. The water is next to the diver's body and is quickly heated by the body heat.

Fig. 21–1.
Why is this suit called a wet suit?

3–5 TO BREATHE UNDER WATER...

Will there come a time when humans will breathe the way fish do? One development is the *SILICONE* (SIL-uh-kone) membrane, with which a hamster was kept alive breathing under water. The membrane works on the same principle as the fish gill. Oxygen passes into the membrane and to the hamster. Carbon dioxide produced by the hamster passes out of the water. Perhaps a special membrane will be produced for humans. Imagine, breathing under water!

Another very exciting possibility is *liquid breathing*. A scientist has been able to get mice and dogs to become "liquid breathers." He placed the animals in a weak salt solution containing large quantities of oxygen, which was pumped in under pressure. The same experiment was tried on a human. He was able to take seven breaths when his lungs were filled with this liquid. Perhaps someday we shall all be able to breathe under water.

- Diving depth is limited by temperature, pressure, and lack of oxygen.
- Diving suits solve some problems, but the diver is not "free."
- Scuba frees the diver by giving him an air supply.
- Diving suits are a new form of protection.
- Face masks protect the diver's face and swim fins help increase speed under water.

3–6 HALF A MILE DOWN!

"August 11, 1934: At 11:12 A.M., we came to rest gently at 3,000 feet." These were the words of Dr. William Beebe, the famous oceanographer. After many earlier dives, he made a record dive in a steel chamber called a *BATHYSPHERE* (BATH-uh-sfeer). Dr. Beebe had reached a point at the bottom of the ocean where no man had ever been before.

The sphere was attached to the ship by a wire cable. The men inside could not control the movement. That was forty years ago. New vessels have been built; new diving methods have been developed. Our knowledge has increased.

Scientists needed a vessel that was not attached by a cable— a vessel that could dive and come up on its own. Now we have such vessels!

Fig. 22–1. The bathysphere in which Dr. William Beebe and Otis Barton made many famous dives. Why was this device important?

3–7 DEEP-SEA DIVING VESSELS

Take a large steel sphere; place into it all the modern conveniences (electricity, telephones). Then attach it to a large *HULL* filled with gasoline. What do you have? A *BATHYSCAPHE* (BATH-uh-skaf). This is essentially what scientists Auguste and Jacques Piccard (pee-KAR) did when they built the bathyscaphe. They called it the *Trieste*. The float of the bathyscaphe has 13 tanks, 11 of which are filled with 30,000 gallons of gasoline. The gasoline is lighter than water, and this makes the craft light enough to float. One tank at each end is left empty until just before the dive. Then the tanks are opened and

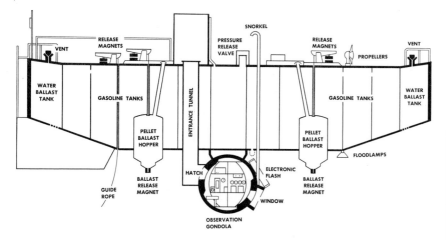

FIG. 23–1. The *Trieste* made one of the deepest dives in history, over 38,000 feet down. How does this craft differ from a bathysphere?

seawater flows in. The bathyscaphe begins to sink. As the vessel goes deeper, the gasoline is compressed in the tanks. This leaves some empty space. Seawater can then enter to occupy this space.

The *trieste* also carries 10 tons of small steel pellets. By releasing some of the pellets, the boat becomes lighter, and it slows down. To rise to the surface, the pellets are released rapidly. This makes the craft lighter, and so it floats.

The men in the *Trieste* reached a depth that no one had ever reached before—over 38,000 feet down.

3–8   THE RESEARCH SUBMARINES

When most people think of submarines, they think of a massive undersea boat used in times of war. In the past few years, submarines have been developed to carry a few people in the exploration of the sea. These subs are very useful because they need no attachment to the surface ship.

The first of these vessels to be developed was the diving saucer called *Denise*. Built by Jacques Cousteau, the saucer is operated by two people. One of its drawbacks is that it can be used only in the shallow waters of the continental shelf.

After the *Denise* came a whole line of craft called *DEEP-STAR SUBMERSIBLES* (sub-MUR-suh-bulz). The first one produced was called *DS-4000*. The four digits stand for the depth it can reach. The submarine is designed to carry a crew of three and is driven by electric motors.

Then came the *ALUMINAUT* (uh-LOO-muh-nawt). It is built of high-strength aluminum alloy. It can reach a depth of 15,000 feet.

FIG. 24–1.

3–9 RESEARCH SUBS IN ACTION

The date was January, 1966. A B-52 bomber carrying an H-bomb crashed near the Spanish Coast. A research sub just large enough for two was used to recover the bomb. This sub, nicknamed *ALVIN*, could reach a depth of 6,000 feet. It had a mechanical arm in front which could grasp objects.

Scientists have built a submarine specially equipped to study the mysteries of ocean currents. It was named the *Ben Franklin,* to honor the man who first studied the currents of the Gulf Stream (Section 2–6). In August, 1969, the sub completed a 30-day voyage. The *Franklin* started its journey off Palm Beach, Florida, and finished it near the coast of Nova Scotia. During this time, scientists aboard measured the course and speed of the Gulf Stream.

Fig. 25–1. The scientists aboard the *Ben Franklin* studied the speed and direction of the Gulf Stream.

The speed of the current was sometimes measured at 4.5 miles per hour—almost twice as fast as had been expected. The scientists on board found marine life to be pretty scarce. But they did sight some sharks, a 30-foot jellyfish, a squid, and a pair of swordfish! One of the most interesting discoveries was that the stream has strong waves.

3–10   A SHIP THAT STANDS!

Just think, a 355-foot ship that can stand on its end with 35 feet of it sticking out of the water! This is the vessel named *FLIP* or *FLoating Instrument Platform*. The upper part of the vessel contains the living and working quarters for the scientists and crew. When the crew wants the lower half to submerge, they flood the *BALLAST TANKS* (BAL-ust). The stern of the ship then sinks under water. *FLIP* is then free to float with the ocean current and is hardly affected by waves. In this position, scientists can take many measurements.

Fig. 25–2. When the ballast tanks are flooded, *FLIP* enters the water. What advantages does *FLIP* have over conventional boats?

LEARNED SO FAR

- Underwater spheres and submarines can bring scientists to great depths for research and study.
- Submersibles can stay under water a long time.
- Submersibles are equipped with many scientific instruments for underwater research.

Self-Study Guide for Chapter 3

I. KNOWING AND UNDERSTANDING. FIND THE ANSWER. WRITE IT IN YOUR NOTEBOOK.

    1. Scuba gear permits the diver to remain under water because
      a. an air line is connected to the surface.
      b. tanks of air are carried with him.
      c. he breathes through membranes.
      d. he holds his breath.
    2. The water in a diver's wet suit
      a. is heated by the diver's body temperature.
      b. is cooled by outside temperature.
      c. provides oxygen for the diver.
      d. is warmed by the air.
    3. In order to make the bathyscaphe descend, the operator must
      a. release steel pellets.
      b. release gasoline.
      c. let seawater enter the hull.
      d. remove seawater from the hull.
    4. The artificial breathing membrane permits
      a. carbon dioxide to pass in from the water.
      b. oxygen to pass in; carbon dioxide out.
      c. both oxygen and carbon dioxide to pass in.
      d. oxygen to pass out.

II. FIND THE EXPLANATION. IN WHICH SECTION OF THE CHAPTER IS THE ANSWER TO EACH OF THE FOLLOWING QUESTIONS? WRITE THE QUESTION AND THE ANSWER IN YOUR NOTEBOOK.

    1. How does the wet suit protect the diver from cold water?
    2. How do the steel pellets enable the bathyscaphe to surface?
    3. What advantage does *FLIP* have over other ships?
    4. What is the function of the scuba diver's regulator?

III. STUDY THE PHOTO ON PAGE 20. ANSWER THE QUESTIONS BELOW IN YOUR NOTEBOOK.

    1. This diver is obtaining her air from a —————— on her back.
    2. The diver is using equipment called —————.
    3. If the diver was swimming in very cold water, she would wear a ———.

UNIT II

The Marine Environment

WHAT'S IT ALL ABOUT?

It is 6 miles deep, or it is covered with but a few
   inches of water . . .
It can be very salty, or just slightly salty . . .
The waters may rise six stories, or ripple gently
   as a quiet lake . . .
It has been called *cruel* and *pacific* . . .
It is both *enemy* and *friend* . . .
It has been used and misused . . .

What are we talking about? Yes—the oceans, the seas, the
bays. What is the sea like? What is it made of? What are the
forces at work in the oceans?

In UNIT II, we shall study the chemistry of seawater. We
shall examine the roaring waves and their crash against the
shores. We shall see how shorelines are shaped. We shall study
the deepest ocean mysteries: What are the ocean bottoms like?
How deep are they? What is their form and their origin? We
shall follow the rise and fall of the tides. We shall investigate
the factors in the sea to set the stage for our later study of life
in the sea.

FIG. 27–1.

CHAPTER 4

PROBLEM:
*What is the shape of
the sea bottom?*

4–1 EXPLORING THE BOTTOM OF THE OCEANS

When we speak of the surface of the earth, we speak of its *TOPOGRAPHY* (tuh-POG-ruh-fee). This concerns heights (mountains), depths (canyons), and shape. The study of these features of the ocean floor is also called topography.

We have learned much about the ocean floor. Divers gave us our first clues. Later, echo soundings and instruments gave us more accurate information. Now, with well-developed U.R.V.'s (Underwater Research Vehicles), we are becoming much more informed.

Let's see what we now know about the ocean's underwater surface.

4–2 MOUNTAINS, CANYONS, AND PLAINS

If all of the water in the oceans were to disappear, what would we see? Mountains taller than the highest ones on the continents! Canyons deeper than the Grand Canyon! Plains greater than those in the West!

We would see the shape of the land below the waters. The study of land shapes is called *TOPOGRAPHY*.

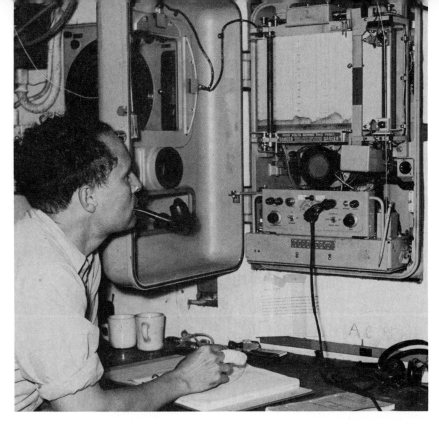

Fig. 29–1. Ocean topography is studied through echo sounding. The equipment is called *SONAR* (SO-nar) (SOund-Navigation-and-Range). The sound machine makes the beeps. The *Hydrophone* receives them on board. A third part figures the distance.

Let's start with the bottom. The bottom of the ocean floor is called the ocean *BASIN* (BAY-sin). Let us imagine that we have a special bus which can take us safely into the underwater basin. This vehicle can travel slowly across the ocean bottom. Where shall we start? A good place would be where the land meets the sea.

4–3 PLAINS OF SAND AND MUD

Our bus enters a world that looks very flat. A closer look shows us large boulders (rocks) here and there. The bus seems to be going downhill, gently, to reach a depth of about 600 feet. This is the area known as the *CONTINENTAL SHELF* (kon-tuh-NEN-tul). This "shelf" stretches out from the land as far as the eye can see. The average distance of the shelf from the shore ranges from 30 to 40 miles. In some places, such as the Grand Banks of Newfoundland, it may stretch for hundreds of miles.

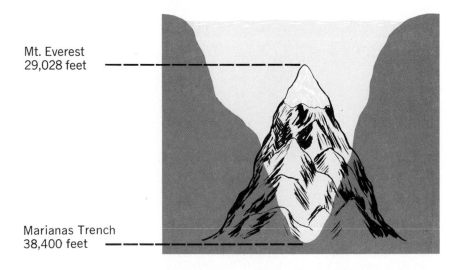

Mt. Everest
29,028 feet

Marianas Trench
38,400 feet

FIG. 30–1. Mt. Everest, the tallest on earth, would be covered if it were placed in the Marianas Trench. By how many feet of water would it be covered?

4–4 AN EXTENSION OF LAND

How was the continental shelf formed? Here's a simple explanation.

A pile of sand and gravel was dumped near your school for a new building. A few days of heavy rain follow. If you now look at the pile, there are little channels or *GULLIES* (GUL-eez) on the pile. As the rainwater flowed across the pile, it carried away tiny sand particles. What you have seen is natural *EROSION* (ee-RO-zhun). Erosion is the wearing away of land as water flows over it. The rivers on land carry tons of particles of sand and soil out to sea. The sand settles in layers called *SEDIMENTS* (SED-uh-ments). This is how the continental shelf is formed.

4–5 LAND CAN BE WORN AWAY

Scientific studies, and even simple observations, show us quickly that the "solid land" is not so solid. Even land can be worn away!

INVESTIGATION: How can we measure how much land is worn away?

PROCEDURES
1. Find some open land near school, home, or in a park.
2. On your school grounds, look for places where rainwater has run over the soil. Find a slope containing gullies about 2 inches wide.
3. With a ruler, measure the length, width, and depth of the gully before a rainstorm.
4. After a rain, measure the length, width, and depth of the same gully.

OBSERVATIONS AND ANALYSIS
1. What happened to the gully after the rain? Is it deeper? Wider?
2. What happened to the materials carried away?
3. Use your observation to explain how the continental shelf was formed.

4–6 DOWN TO THE DEPTHS

Let us now look out of the bus window again. Having left the flat plain, our bus is now going downhill. We have approached a very steep cliff. The water continues to get deeper. This is the area of the sea known as the *CONTINENTAL SLOPE*. As we approach the 10,000-foot mark, we enter another world.

4–7 CANYONS IN THE SEA

When you think of a canyon, what comes to mind? The Grand Canyon in Colorado? The street "canyons" of Manhattan or Detroit or St. Louis? As we said before, the sea also has its canyons. A canyon is a deep valley with very steep sides. The sea's canyons may be as wide and as deep as any found on the land. Along many parts of the continental shelf and slope, deep canyons slice through the sediments. These are called *SUBMARINE CANYONS*. They are often found where large river systems flow into the sea. One canyon that has been explored in great detail is the Hudson River Canyon. It is named after the great river that enters the sea at New York City.

FIG. 32–1. The ocean bottom has a definite shape to it. How was the continental shelf formed?

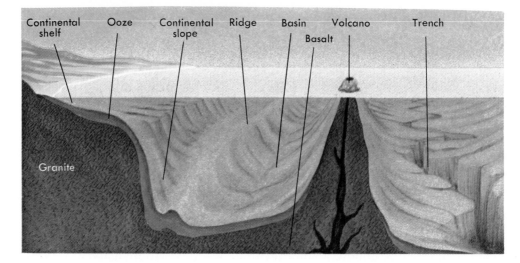

LEARNED SO FAR

● The oceans fill huge depressions in the earth's surface. These depressions are known as basins.
● The flat, *gently* sloping area of the sea is called the continental shelf.
● The continental slope lies at the end of the shelf and is very steep.
● Canyons can be found where large river systems flow into the sea.

4–8 A PROBLEM IN OCEANOGRAPHY

How were underwater canyons formed? We know that the Grand Canyon was formed by the Colorado River, carving away at the rock. Were the continental shelves once above the sea? Did the rivers carve the canyons as they do on the land? This is one theory some scientists support.

Another theory is that canyons were cut into the shelves by great underwater currents of silt and sand. These great currents of sand caused the bottom deposits to be carried away. They are given the name *TURBIDITY CURRENTS* (tur-BID-uh-tee).

What theory would you accept? Most scientists favor the turbidity-current idea.

4–9 LAND OF DARKNESS

Again, let us get back to our underwater bus ride. The continental slope led us to a very deep and dark new world. We now look around with our powerful floodlights and see a flat plain. Traveling across the plain reminds us of the continental shelf—except that it is very deep. This is the land of the *ABYSS* (uh-BIS).

Fig. 33–1. Photograph of the abyss taken by the undersea vessel *Trieste*. Picture was taken at a depth of 2,715 feet. The animals are *brittle stars* and *sea cucumbers*. How is the abyss similar to the shelf? How is it different?

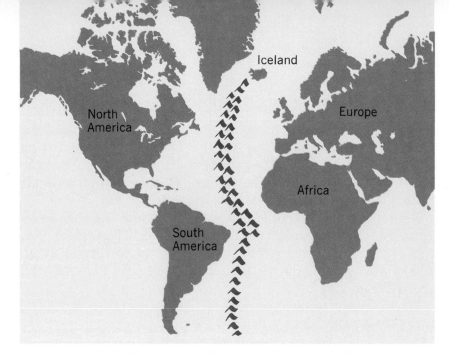

FIG. 34–1. The Mid-Atlantic Ridge cuts the Atlantic into two parts. Can we call these mountains? Why?

If we continue our journey across the abyss we will find scenery as beautiful as any on land. Oceanographers have discovered huge mountain ranges rising out of the dark plains. In the Atlantic Ocean, there is a mountain range that has an average height of 5,450 feet. It is about 200 miles wide. This is the *MID-ATLANTIC RIDGE*. It runs the entire length of the Atlantic and then turns around Africa, where it joins a similar mountain range in the Indian Ocean. The Pacific also has a ridge. Scientists think that these midocean ridges were formed from lava poured out by volcanoes millions of years ago. In many places, ridges rise above the sea to form islands. Get a map of Europe and the Atlantic Ocean. Locate the islands of Iceland and the Azores. These are two examples of island ridges.

4–10 A DEEP PLUNGE

Take 35 Empire State Buildings and line them up end to end. This would give us a rough idea of how deep some of the deepest parts of the oceans are. In some parts of our world the continental slope plunges downward to the greatest depths of the oceans. These are called the *TRENCHES*.

SOME WELL-KNOWN OCEAN TRENCHES

Name	Located Near	Depth
Marianas	Guam	38,400 ft.
Philippine	Philippines	32,800 ft.
Nares	Puerto Rico	30,216 ft.
Middle America	Eastern Pacific	21,851 ft.

On January 22, 1960, the scientist Jacques Piccard and Navy Lt. Don Walsh traveled 38,400 feet down to the bottom of the *MARIANAS* Trench. They made their journey in a special craft called the *Trieste*. We now know that the Marianas Trench is 38,400 feet deep.

How big are trenches? Some of them are 100 miles long and 100 miles wide! All in all, there are 17 well-known trenches.

LEARNED SO FAR

- The deepest part of the ocean is known as the abyss.
- Underwater mountain ranges are called ridges.
- Deep cuts in the ocean floor are known as trenches.

I. KNOWING AND UNDERSTANDING. FIND THE ANSWER. WRITE
    IT IN YOUR NOTEBOOK.

    1. The sediments of the continental shelf
       a. were formed by volcanic action.
       b. were formed by land materials carried to the sea.
       c. came from the deep sea.
       d. came from outer space.
    2. Submarine canyons are usually found where
       a. the land meets the sea.
       b. you find seamounts.
       c. rivers enter the sea.
       d. there are mountain ranges.
    3. Scientists believe submarine canyons were formed by
       a. turbidity currents cutting at the sediments.
       b. volcanic eruptions causing the land to split.
       c. the land splitting.
       d. movements of the earth's crust.
    4. The abyss differs from the continental shelf mostly in that it is
       a. closer to the land.
       b. very shallow.
       c. the deepest part of the ocean.
       d. cut by canyons.

II. FIND THE EXPLANATION. IN WHICH SECTION OF THE CHAP-
    TER IS THE ANSWER TO EACH OF THE FOLLOWING QUES-
    TIONS? WRITE THE QUESTION AND THE ANSWER IN YOUR
    NOTEBOOK.

    1. Why is the continental shelf made up of particles from the land?
    2. How do currents cause submarine canyons to form?
    3. Why is the abyss not a flat plain?
    4. Why is it important to know about volcanoes when you discuss
       underwater mountain ranges?

III. WHICH IS THE OUTSIDER? ONE WORD IN THE LIST DOES NOT
     BELONG WITH THE OTHER TWO. WRITE THE WORD.

     1. Continental shelf, sediments, abyss.
     2. Submarine canyons, turbidity currents, bathysphere.
     3. Abyss, Mid-Atlantic Ridge, continental shelf.

IV. WHICH COMES FIRST? ARRANGE THE FOUR PROCESSES IN THE ORDER IN WHICH THEY OCCUR.

    a. Settling of sediments in the ocean.
    b. Breakdown of rocks.
    c. Transfer of particles to rivers.
    d. Transfer of particles to streams.

V. OCEANOGRAPHY HALL OF FAME. STATE HOW EACH OF THE FOLLOWING SCIENTISTS HELPED US UNDERSTAND OCEANOGRAPHY.

    a. Matthew Fontaine Maury.
    b. Edward Forbes.
    c. Benjamin Franklin.
    d. Jacques Piccard.

VI. WHAT'S THE DIFFERENCE? COMPARE THE WORDS. STATE THE DIFFERENCE BETWEEN WORDS IN EACH PAIR.

    1. Trench—ridge.
    2. Continental shelf—continental slope.
    3. Submarine canyon—Grand Canyon.

VII. RESEARCH ABOUT RESEARCH. USING A RECENT ENCYCLOPEDIA OR A BOOK ON OCEANOGRAPHY, LOOK UP THE *MOHO PROJECT*. PREPARE A REPORT TO INCLUDE THE FOLLOWING:

    1. What is the Moho?
    2. What did the project do? How long did it last?
    3. What did they find out?
    4. Why was it discontinued?

CHAPTER 5

Ocean Sediments: Soils of the Deep

PROBLEM:
What are ocean sediments made of?

5–1 MAKE THE BLUE PIGEON FLY!

The time is two hundred years ago. A sailing ship is caught in a thick fog. A voice shouts, "Make the blue pigeon fly!" A sailor tosses a weighted cuplike object overboard. Attached to the cup is a sticky substance known as tallow. The tallow causes the materials on the sea bottom to stick to it. Afterward, the "blue pigeon" is hauled aboard ship and the muds and sands are examined. A muddy or sandy bottom told mariners that they might be close to the shore. Why would mud or sand be found near the shore?

Unlike our sailor of years ago, scientists study the bottom to learn how it was formed and of what it is made. In this chapter, we shall learn that this knowledge can give us clues as to how the earth was formed. It will also help us to understand what forms of life there may have been millions of years ago.

5–2 LAYER AFTER LAYER

What would our world be like if it snowed day after day? What if the snow never melted? We might enjoy ourselves because it would mean sledding, skiing, and snowball fights. But this fun wouldn't last long, for the snow would eventually get too deep. At the very bottom of our pile would be the first layer, with layer after layer above it.

The same type of layering has been going on in the ocean for thousands of years. Instead of snow, there are a great variety of things that have settled to the bottom. There are sediments carried from the land by river systems. There are remains of dead animals and plants. Even the dust from space has fallen into the sea. A shower of particles is forever settling into the sea. It is like our snowfall which never stops.

5-3 WHEN SEDIMENTS SETTLE

Common sediment carried by a river includes pebbles, sand, and clay (mud). Sooner or later these sediments will settle to the bottom. Which ones will settle first?

DO AND DISCOVER

INVESTIGATION: How do the sediments of rivers settle in the sea?

PROCEDURES
1. Take a tall container. Pour water into it. Now drop small pebbles, sand, and clay into the water.
2. Stir well; let it stand for a day.

OBSERVATIONS AND ANALYSIS
1. Which material settles first? Next? Last?
2. Why do the materials settle in this order?
3. Based on this investigation, how can you explain why you might find a sand bar near a river mouth and mud and silt farther out to sea.

5-4 ON THE SHELF

A dredge, as you may remember from your earlier reading, is a special shovel that can scoop up material from a river or sea bottom. It is lowered into the ocean at the end of a cable.

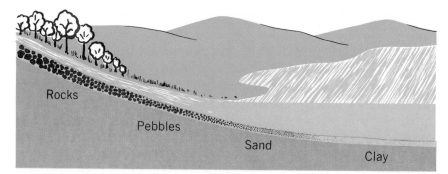

FIG. 40–1. What does this settling tell us about the continental shelf?

Then the dredge is dragged along the ocean bottom. As the ship moves, the dredge scoops material from the bottom. Later, the dredge is hoisted up on the cable. The materials are removed from the dredge for observation and study.

What do samples from the continental shelf show? Sands and muds may be present and come mostly from rivers and from wave action on the shore. If a sample is taken where a river enters the sea, we shall find pebbles and larger particles deposited first. Then, a little farther out, we would find sand. Finer particles, such as silt and mud, would be found some distance from the river's mouth.

Why do the different sediments settle out at different rates? Pebbles and rocks are much heavier than sand and mud. They would sink much faster and so would be found closer to the shore. Muds and silts are lighter and would be carried farther out to sea. Why do we find sand bars where a river enters the sea?

5–5   DEEP-SEA OOZE

Some parts of the sea have been described as a "thick soup." The ingredients of the "soup" are water, dissolved chemicals, and billions of tiny animals and plants. When these organisms die and leave their remains, they are then called *FOSSILS* (FOS-ulz). A good portion of these remains are found in the shallower parts of the abyss. The "thick soup" also called "ooze" contains much lime (calcium carbonate) from microscopic animals.

FIG. 40–2.
Fossils. Explain how they were formed. What do they show?

If we took our samples from the deeper parts of the abyss, we would find claylike sediments. When scientists first collected samples of this material, it appeared red. It was thus given the name *RED CLAY*. Most often it is brown in color. This clay is made up of land dust, volcanic dust, and traces of *METE-ORITES* (rocks) from outer space.

WHERE DO SEDIMENTS COME FROM?

Place Found	Type	Origin	Approximate Thickness
Continental shelf	Sands, muds, pebbles	From land	12,000 feet
Shallow abyss	Lime	Skeletons of animals and plants	1,200 feet
Deep abyss	Red clay	Dust, volcanic dust, meteorite dust	300 to 600 feet

5–6 THE ROCKY BOTTOM

Let us examine the composition of the earth. Figure 41–1 shows our earth in cross section.

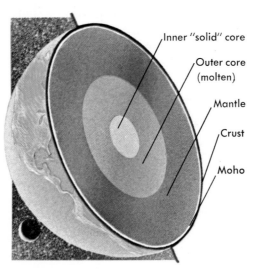

Inner "solid" core

Outer core (molten)

Mantle

Crust

Moho

Fig. 41–1.
The earth in cross section. Look up Moho and read about how it is important in studying oceanography.

Suppose we got to the very bottom of the ocean. What would we find there? The *bedrock* of the ocean: the ocean basins of basalt rock. The basalt rock is part of the earth's crust. The earth's crust on land is about 30 miles thick. Under the oceans, it is about 3 miles thick.

LEARNED SO FAR

- Many materials on the land that is below ocean water come from the land.
- Sea fossils are the remains of the sea life of long ago.
- The ocean bottom is in the form of ridges, canyons, volcanoes, and trenches.

5–7 USING THE CORER

Make a sphere (ball) of soft red and gray clay (see Figure 42–1). Now *slowly* bore (push) a strong glass tube into the clay. Pull the borer out *very slowly*. You now have withdrawn a sample of the "mud" or clay. This is the idea behind the *corer* we learned about in Chapter 2.

This is what oceanographers try to do when they send a coring instrument into the sediments. At first, the corer was simply a large tube with a weight on it. These instruments rarely went very deep. As a result, the sediments brought to the surface were from the top layers. Afterward, the *PISTON CORER* was developed. When this instrument is lowered into the water, a hanging weight pulls it down to the bottom. As it hits the bottom, it signals the core tube to slide past a piston. The result is that a sample of sediment is sucked into the tube. Sediments over 60 feet in length can be forced into the tube.

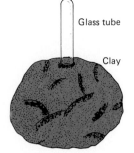

Glass tube

Clay

Fig. 42–1.
The core in the tube shows *two* things. What are they?

5–8 MARKING OFF TIME

How old is the earth? How was the earth formed? What types of life lived in ancient seas? You have probably learned about

42

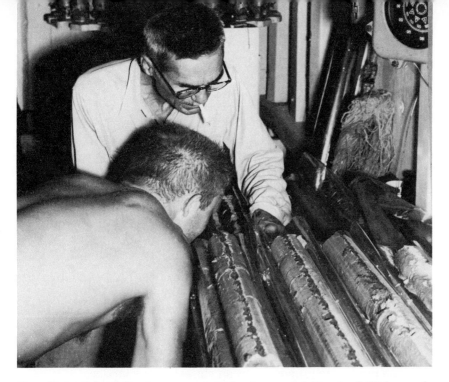

FIG. 43–1. Scientists store core samples in special "banks." This one is The Lamont Geology Library in Palisades, New York. What do core samples tell the scientist? Oceanographers share their work with fellow scientists. They contribute core samples to geology research laboratories where they can be studied by others.

the many ways in which scientists estimate the age of the earth. Ocean corers are also useful in solving this problem. Every time a scientist sends a corer a few feet into the sediments, he goes back thousands of years into earth history.

Let's try a little problem ourselves. Suppose you were examining a core sample collected in a cold region of the world. Upon closer examination, you find the remains of animals which lived in warmer parts of the world. What theory could you form about the climate of this area thousands of years ago?

This is one way in which scientists read the core samples. For those who know the "language of the cores," the stories that cores tell can be very exciting.

LEARNED SO FAR

● Core samples may be stored in "banks."
● Cores give us clues to the past.

Self-Study Guide for Chapter 5

I. KNOWING AND UNDERSTANDING. FIND THE ANSWER. WRITE IT IN YOUR NOTEBOOK.

1. Rivers carry mud and silt farther out to sea because
   a. the particles are heavier and are carried farther.
   b. the particles are lighter and are carried farther.
   c. pebbles push them out farther.
   d. they cannot sink in shallow water.
2. In a section of sediment, the deepest layers
   a. are much older than the surface layer.
   b. are much younger than the surface layer.
   c. are much heavier.
   d. consist of animal life.
3. The land from under the ocean closest to the land is
   a. the Moho.
   b. the continental slope.
   c. the ridge.
   d. the continental shelf.
4. A corer helps the scientist collect deposits in the correct order of formation because
   a. it spreads out the sample.
   b. it traps the sample in layers.
   c. it determines their age.
   d. it labels them.

II. FIND THE EXPLANATION. IN WHICH SECTION OF THE CHAPTER IS THE ANSWER TO EACH OF THE FOLLOWING QUESTIONS? WRITE THE QUESTION AND THE ANSWER IN YOUR NOTEBOOK.

1. How could ancient mariners find their direction by sampling the sediments?
2. How do we find materials from the land deposited on the continental shelf?
3. How can scientists study ocean sediments in the order in which they were formed?

III. WHAT'S WRONG WITH THE DIAGRAM BELOW? IN YOUR NOTE-BOOK, WRITE A FEW SENTENCES TELLING WHAT IS WRONG WITH THIS DIAGRAM.

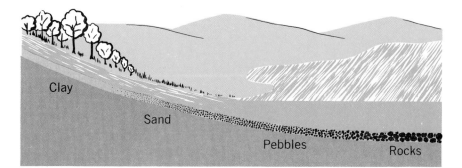

Clay

Sand

Pebbles

Rocks

FIG. 45–1.

IV. STUDY THE INVESTIGATION ON PAGE 39. ANSWER THE QUES-TIONS IN YOUR NOTEBOOK.

    1. Why are sand bars usually found at harbor entrances?
    2. Why is mud carried farther out to sea?

V. PLAN A FIELD TRIP.

If you live near ocean waters, visit a spot where a creek or river enters the bay. Look for any evidence of sediment deposits. Look first for sand and pebbles. Then search for silt and muds. Collect samples in bottles. Label them.

VI. DO YOU LIKE POETRY?

Ask your English teacher to recommend three poems about the sea. Read them. Can you find a few lines that describe some of the things you have learned so far?

CHAPTER 6

Shaping the Shores

PROBLEM:
How are shorelines formed?

6–1 THE SHORES OF OUR OCEANS

What does a beach mean to you? To some, it's a place to spread out a blanket and catch some sun. To others, it's a place for a refreshing swim or perhaps a thrilling ride on a surfboard. For the surf fisherman, it is a place to catch "the big ones."

Nations, peoples, and history have been affected by their shores. Harbors have been used to develop commerce. Armies have battled on shores to invade or defend them.

Today, oceanographers and environmental scientists study shores to prevent erosion, to "farm" the sea for its minerals and food, and to obtain fresh water and even electric power.

6–2 THE FACE OF THE SHORE

Many people think of a beach as a white, smooth, sandy stretch of land at the seashore. Not so! In the first place, beach sand may be silver-white, golden brown, or dark black. There are beaches of jagged rock. There are beaches of huge rounded boulders. There are beaches in which there are caves and cliffs and towers reaching to the sky. In other places, there are mud beaches, so soft your feet can sink into them.

Some shorelines are straight; some are curvy and uneven. Some have islands offshore, and some have long narrow bars of sand peeking out of the water. Some beaches have silver-white coral just offshore.

FIG. 46–1.

How has all this happened? Some people say the sea is a sculptor; that the waters, in the form of tides and waves, are like chisels hammering away at the land . . . year after year . . . century after century. Let's see how shores are shaped.

6-3 SHIFTING SANDS

There are two moving forces that shift the sands. Back at the beach, you may have had the experience of feeling a sudden gust of wind. The result was a faceful of sand. At the shore, the pounding waves move the sediments of the sea to the shore and carry bits of the shore into the sea.

Each time a wave hits the beach, it carries with it large amounts of sediment. Near the water's edge you can find evidence of what the waves may carry toward the shore. This is called the *STRAND LINE*. If you search through it, you may find that it is made up mainly of seaweeds, driftwood, and other remains. It also provides a home for living things.

FIG. 47-1. Advancing surf threatens homes in Fort Pierce, Florida. How could this have been prevented?

FIG. 47-2. A rocky shoreline in Maine. Will this shoreline look the same in the year 2274? Explain.

INVESTIGATION: How can we observe the changing of an ocean-front beach?

PROCEDURES

1. Visit an oceanfront beach on a pleasant day. If you are not near an ocean, try using a shoreline on a lake.
2. Write in your notebook some of its outstanding features —for example, dunes, line of shrubs, and so on.
3. Take photos if you can.
4. Return to the same spot after a storm or on a windy day.
5. Look for any changes in the environment.

OBSERVATIONS AND ANALYSIS

1. Have any of the landmarks changed?
2. Has the shape of the beach changed?
3. Is the strand line in a different area? Is it larger? Smaller?
4. What forces are responsible for these changes?

6–4 HOW ARE SHORELINES FORMED?

Did you know that our first President, George Washington, was once a land *SURVEYOR* (sur-VAY-ur)? In the early 1700's he was called upon to plan the lighthouse at Montauk Point, Long Island. Washington predicted that it would take the sea about two hundred years to reach the base of the lighthouse. This is exactly what is happening now. Plans are now being made to stop this erosion; otherwise, the whole lighthouse will be in danger.

The action of the water changes the scenery on the shore. Rocks are torn away. Water jumps hundreds of feet into cracks. The moving water hurls sand and pebbles against the rocks, grinding the rock surfaces. Sometimes the sea can throw very heavy rocks up on the shore.

Fig. 49–1. The shoreline has been "creeping up" to reach the Montauk Point Lighthouse.

LEARNED SO FAR

● The shape of the shore is formed by the natural forces of erosion.
● Waves carry large amounts of sediment and other materials to the shores.
● Things carried ashore by the waves collect at the strand line.

6–5 TYPES OF SHORES

Some shorelines stick out into the ocean in a crazy zigzag way. These are the *headlands*. Other shores push inward to form *bays*.

When the waves strike directly against a rocky shoreline, they "bite" and shape the land. As a result of this action, a *WAVE-CUT CLIFF* may form. Erosion causes the rocks at the base of the cliff to break away. The rocks then accumulate near the base of the cliff, causing a *WAVE-CUT TERRACE*. Over the years, these terraces may get very large and extend many feet into the sea. When the waves cut deeply into a cliff, a *SEA CAVE* may form.

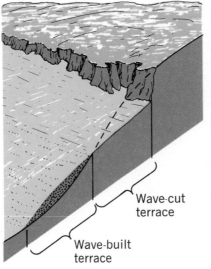 

Fig. 50-1.
How is a wave-cut terrace formed?

Fig. 50-2.
Wave-cut cliffs. What caused the rocks to take on this shape?

A shoreline that has many of these sea cliffs is called an *EMERGENT* (ee-MUR-junt) shoreline. Geologists feel that at one time the sea level fell. This left the land exposed and open to erosion by waves.

If a shoreline has many bays and inlets, it is called *SUB-MERGENT* (sub-MUR-junt). The theory is that millions of years ago the sea level rose. The result was that land valleys got filled in with water. These valleys are called *DROWNED RIVER VALLEYS*. A drowned river valley with an opening to the sea is called an *ESTUARY* (ES-chuh-wair-ee).

6-6 BUILDING IT UP

We have just described how shorelines are broken down to be shaped and reshaped. But shorelines can also be built up because of sand deposits. When a wave breaks along a beach, it carries sand and gravel with it. Some of this material is deposited on the beach. Sometimes these particles of sand are carried out to sea again.

The sand is deposited in small hills at the bottom of shallow offshore water. The sand slowly forms a *BAR*—a narrow strip of sandy land. Gradually, the bar rises out of the water to form

50

an *OFFSHORE BAR*. Between the bar and the mainland, quiet, shallow water remains. This forms a *LAGOON*. These bars are found all along the Atlantic coast. Miami Beach, Florida, and Jones Beach, New York, are two famous offshore bars. Great South Bay is the lagoon behind Fire Island, off the southern shore of Long Island, New York.

FIG. 51–1. Miami Beach, Florida, was built on an offshore bar. How is a bar formed?

6–7 LAND FROM LIVING ANIMALS

Have you ever seen *CORAL* (KAR-ul)? These are the white lime skeletons of sea animals. We shall refer to them again in a later chapter.

As corals grow, they take lime from the sea and build their shells. The corals die; but their skeletons remain and build up tiny islands or *REEFS*, which grow close to shore. Such a reef, offshore, acts like a bar. It shelters the water between it and the mainland to form a quiet, shallow *LAGOON*. The largest reef in the world is the Great Barrier Reef on the northeastern shore of Australia. It is 1,200 miles long; in spots, it is 90 miles wide!

FIG. 51–2. Tiny islands or reefs formed from the skeletons of corals.

FIG. 52–1. How does the lagoon help the marine life? How do we know coral islands were once alive?

In the Pacific Ocean, corals have formed ring-shaped islands which enclose quiet lagoons. These rings of land are called *ATOLLS* (A-tohlz). They probably grew around volcanoes which are sunk below the water.

6–8 CONTROL OF SHORE EROSION

We are constantly waging a battle to control erosion of valuable beach areas. We build *jetties* of stone and wood to prevent currents from eroding shorelines. Beach plants are planted along the dunes. The roots of these plants bind the sand and slow down blowing and shifting. This battle will continue for as long as people live and work near the sea.

LEARNED SO FAR

- Shores may show headlands or bays.
- Current action forms bays, terraces, and cliffs.
- Some shores have estuaries, which are drowned river valleys.
- The sea currents also build land in the form of sand bars, coral reefs, and coral atolls.
- Man has a permanent job to control erosion of shorelines.

Self-Study Guide for Chapter 6

I. KNOWING AND UNDERSTANDING. FIND THE ANSWER. WRITE IT IN YOUR NOTEBOOK.

1. We may find evidence of what a pounding surf has done to a rocky shore by looking for
   a. attached animals.
   b. sand dunes.
   c. sea caves.
   d. mud banks.
2. A sandy beach is shaped by the action of
   a. wind and surf.
   b. animals.
   c. offshore bars.
   d. beach plants.
3. Evidence that waves carry large amounts of materials can be found in the
   a. dune area.
   b. subtidal range.
   c. terrace.
   d. strand line.
4. A coast that has many bays and inlets was formed by
   a. a rising sea level.
   b. a falling sea level.
   c. land rising.
   d. deposits of sediments.

II. FIND THE EXPLANATION. IN WHICH SECTION OF THE CHAPTER IS THE ANSWER TO EACH OF THE FOLLOWING QUESTIONS? WRITE THE QUESTION AND THE ANSWER IN YOUR NOTEBOOK.

1. How are atolls formed?
2. How can we explain the formation of sea cliffs?
3. How can we explain the formation of an estuary?
4. How were shorelines built up?

III. MATCH THE WORDS IN COLUMN *A* WITH THOSE IN COLUMN *B* IN YOUR NOTEBOOK.

A	*B*
1. Estuary	a. Deposits of sand
2. Lime skeleton	b. Control of erosion
3. Emergent shore	c. Shoreline with many sea cliffs
4. Offshore bar	d. Shoreline with bays and inlets
5. Jetty	e. Drowned river mouth
	f . Coral

IV. TRUE OR FALSE? EXPLAIN YOUR ANSWERS.

1. A sea cave may be found along a sandy beach.
2. An estuary is found in the middle of the ocean.
3. Waves and wind mold our shores.
4. Many famous beach resorts are found on offshore bars.

V. FIND THE OUTSIDER. CHOOSE THE ONE WORD IN THE LIST THAT DOES NOT BELONG WITH THE OTHER TWO. WRITE THE WORD.

1. Waves, currents, lagoon.
2. Sandy beach, strand line, wave-cut terraces.
3. Emergent shore, wave-cut cliffs, submergent shore.
4. River valley, estuary, offshore bar.

VI. ALL ABOUT LIGHTHOUSES. IN AN ENCYCLOPEDIA, FIND OUT:

1. Where the five largest lighthouses in the world are.
2. How lighthouses control harbor ships.
3. What the source of their light is.
4. The difference between a lighthouse and a *buoy*.

CHAPTER 7

Following the Oceans' Currents

PROBLEM:
What are the major ocean currents?

7–1 BERG AHEAD!

The weather was clear and the sea was calm. One of the largest ships afloat was steaming across the North Atlantic. The date was April 14, 1912; the ship, the *Titanic*. At 11:40 at night, the lookouts signaled the captain, "Iceberg ahead!" As the *Titanic* passed along the side of the iceberg, a deep gash was torn into the ship's right side below the water line. The ship took on water quickly. By morning, it was at the bottom and 1,513 people were lost.

Fɪɢ. 55–1. From the *New York Times,* April 16, 1912.

Fig. 56–1. Icebergs are "calved" or begin in the Arctic regions. How do they reach southern waters?

7-2 TRAVELS OF A BERG

Icebergs are formed in the northern seas. How do they move?

After the *Titanic* disaster, the major world powers met and formed the International Ice Patrol—to search out answers. Icebergs start their journey in the northern seas. They are carried southward by moving ocean water. How can the patrol predict an iceberg's drift from the north? To do this, it is necessary to understand the movement of ocean water. We, too, need to learn about these movements as part of our study of oceanography. Let's find out how the ocean's waters flow.

The ocean has many streams of moving water. These are called *CURRENTS*. A current is a moving, streaming, or flowing body of water or air. In fact, currents have been called the "rivers of the ocean." Like rivers on land, ocean currents flow along, almost always keeping to the same course. Ocean currents may be wide and long and cold. As you will see later, there are warm-water currents and cold-water currents.

7-3 SPINNING EARTH AND SPINNING WATER

Next time you're swimming in a pool, look for the water outlet pipe. Stand against it and try to feel the current of water flowing out. Find something that floats; see how far it travels in the stream of water.

The ocean has many currents. Unlike the currents in our swimming pool, these currents are driven mainly by the force of the earth's rotation.

Place a basin of water on a lazy Susan tray or on a rotating piano stool. Spin the basin gently in a counterclockwise direction (left to right). Observe. Let the water rest until it is still. Rotate the basin in the opposite direction.

The experiment above shows how the earth's spinning action creates winds. This same spinning action causes the currents to spin.

7–4   THE SUN AND THE OCEAN'S CURRENTS

The equator of our earth receives direct sun rays. So you can see that the waters near the equator will be warmer than the waters nearer both poles. Differences in water temperature start water movement. In other words, water temperature is another cause of currents. Currents caused by temperature changes are called *CONVECTION* (kon-VEK-shun) currents.

DO AND DISCOVER

INVESTIGATION: How can we show a convection current?

PROCEDURES
1. Fill a baking pan with water. Gently heat one end of the pan with a Bunsen burner.
2. Place several drops of ink or dye on the cool side of the pan.

OBSERVATIONS AND ANALYSIS
1. Which way does the cold water move?
2. When the colored water reaches the warm end of the pan, which way does it move?

The waters near the equator are warm. They expand and produce the *EQUATORIAL CURRENTS* (ee-kwuh-TOR-ee-uhl). Pushed by the winds and the earth's rotation, they move toward the poles. The warmth of this current is transferred to the land and to the cool northern waters. The colder, heavier water sinks and moves back toward the equator.

7-5 MOVEMENT OF CURRENTS

The earth is like a huge ball. If we divide the ball into two equal parts, we have the Northern and Southern *HEMISPHERES* (HEM-uh-sfeerz). The major currents float around these hemispheres in circular patterns called *GYRES* (JY-urz).

North of the equator, the movement of the currents is in a clockwise direction. South of the equator, the movement is counterclockwise. How do we explain this? The currents are being moved by the winds.

The air at the equator, as we have seen, is warmer. The warm air expands, grows lighter, and rises. As it reaches the poles, it cools. The cool air now sinks down to earth and the cycle begins again. As the earth rotates, the wind blows west (clockwise) in the Northern Hemisphere and east (counterclockwise) in the Southern Hemisphere.

In the days of sailing ships, sailors would try to search out the *TRADE WINDS*. Produced by the earth's rotation, these powerful winds would give ships a tremendous boost in speed. Trade winds are the major driving forces of currents in tropical regions. They can reach speeds of 30 to 40 miles per hour. They blow north and southwest, creating the equatorial currents.

LEARNED SO FAR

- Currents are "rivers of water" in the oceans.
- Currents move along regular routes.
- Currents are caused by the triple force of heat, rotation, and wind.

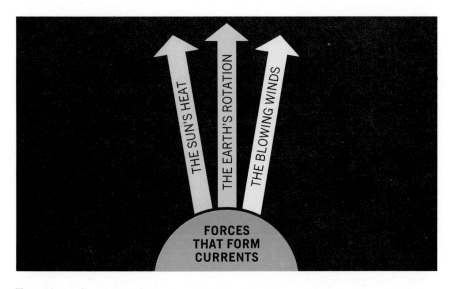

FIG. 59–1. Currents move in definite directions. Which way do they move in the Northern Hemisphere? Why?

7–6   CHARTING THE CURRENTS

In 1770, Benjamin Franklin became interested in currents. He published what was probably the first chart of a current. It was the chart of the Gulf Stream. (Locate the Gulf Stream on the map, Figure 60–1.)

What does a chart of a current show? In addition to its direction (course), its temperature, speed, and depth are very helpful data.

One way to measure the way currents flow is to release *DRIFT BOTTLES* into the water. A drift bottle contains a card that asks the finder to write down where it was found, what the weather was like, and the date and time of discovery. The information is then sent to the person in charge of the project.

Currents that are shallow and very wide may move from ½ mile to 2 miles per hour. Deeper and narrower currents move faster. For example, the Gulf Stream moves about 5 miles per hour.

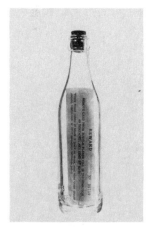

FIG. 59–2. Drift bottles are used to collect information about current flow.

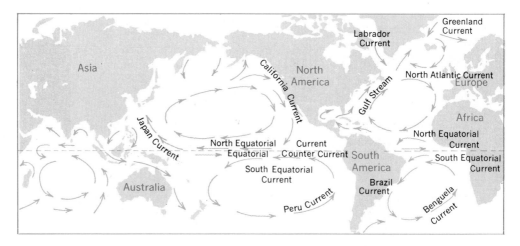

Fig. 60–1. Ocean currents of the world. Warm Currents: Japan, Equatorial, Brazil, Gulf. Cold Currents: Peru (Humboldt), Benguela, Labrador, California, North Atlantic.

7–7 WHO'S WHO AMONG THE CURRENTS?

What are the major ocean currents? As you read this description, follow the map in Figure 60–1 above.

In general, currents that flow *from* the equator are warm. Currents that flow away from the poles and *toward* the equator are cold.

7–8 CURRENTS IN OUR LIVES

How have currents affected us? There are three major ways. In the first place, they determine the course of ships and therefore affect navigation. In the second place, their temperature and speed can affect the climate of the land near which they pass. Finally, currents affect sea life because of their temperature and movement.

Look at the map in Figure 60–1. Find the current that flows along the western coast of South America. This is the Humboldt Current. It is pushed by a westward wind and swings to join the South Equatorial Current. This causes a movement of deeper water to the surface known as *upwelling*. Wherever upwelling occurs, we find a rich supply of minerals which attracts a fantastic number of fish. Peruvian fishermen depend upon upwelling for their living.

And because currents affect navigation, they have affected the migration and settling of people in early history. This often changed the course of history.

7–9 PALM TREES NEAR THE ARCTIC CIRCLE

Who would ever believe that you could find a garden of palm trees growing near the Arctic Circle? Travel to northern Scotland and you can find a collection of these trees. Why are they able to live in this part of the world?

In the Northern Hemisphere, the Equatorial Current passes along the coast of North America to form the Gulf Stream Gyre. The waters of the stream have a warming effect upon the land. The stream also passes very close to the British coast; this makes the average temperature of Scotland 5 to 15 degrees warmer. When the warm air meets the cold air of northern Europe, thick fogs are produced.

If you look at the map, you can see that the British Isles and Labrador are almost the same distance from the North Pole. Yet, thanks to the Gulf Stream, Britain's climate is moderate while Labrador's is very cold.

Now locate the California Current. California is as close to the equator as the Sahara Desert. Yet California's climate is moist and cool and pleasant.

Finally, find the Labrador Current. The arrow shows how it flows along Canada and our New England states.

7–10 THE GRAVEYARD OF SHIPS

Located inside the Gulf Stream, near the West Indies, is an area known as the *SARGASSO SEA* (sar-GAS-so). This vast area of ocean was once called the "graveyard of ships." According to the sailors' tall tales, the ships would become tangled in the thick seaweed called *Sargassum*. Marine biologists who have studied the area have found very little life under the thick growth of seaweed. But if we searched through the *Sargassum*, we would find many creatures that blend into the colors and shapes of the plants. Fish, shrimp, and crabs are just a few of the types of creatures to be found in this seaweed.

Later, we shall see that currents affect both plant and animal life in the sea.

7–11 CURRENTS AND HISTORY

Currents have been known by sailors for thousands of years. Way back in 1513, the Spanish explorer *JUAN PONCE DE LEÓN* (PONS DUH LEE-un) had learned to use the Gulf Stream, which helped his ships sail easily from America back to Spain. By getting into the stream, they were carried a little northward along the east coast of the United States and then across to Europe.

Benjamin Franklin drew his chart of the Gulf Stream to get the ships from England to bring the mail to America much faster. By sailing slightly southward, they could avoid the rush of the current against them.

How did the ancient *Incas*, the proud Indians of Peru, get to the Easter Islands in the South Pacific thousands of miles away? To find out, *Thor Heyerdahl* (HY-ur-dol) built a raft of light wood and set sail from Peru. On the entire trip of 4,300 miles, Heyerdahl and his men let the natural ocean currents move them. After 101 days, they arrived near the island of Tahiti.

FIG. 62–1. You can read about Thor Heyerdahl's thrilling adventure in his book *Kon-Tiki*, which he named after his oceangoing raft.

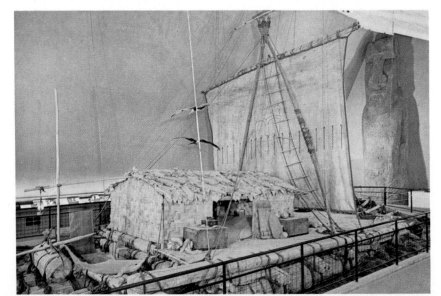

● Currents can be charted as to direction, speed, and temperature.
● The major ocean currents are now known and recorded on maps.
● Ocean currents control sea navigation, sea life, and climate.
● Ocean currents have affected the history of the world.

Self-Study Guide for Chapter 7

I. KNOWING AND UNDERSTANDING. FIND THE ANSWER. WRITE IT IN YOUR NOTEBOOK.

  1. Ocean currents turn clockwise in the Northern Hemisphere because
     a. the ocean waters drive them this way.
     b. bottom currents help them.
     c. winds push them in this direction.
     d. they are pulled by the continents.
  2. Colder water is found near the bottom because
     a. it is pulled down.
     b. it is heavier.
     c. it moves faster.
     d. it is lighter.
  3. A convection current is formed when heat from a warm liquid is transferred to
     a. a cooler liquid.
     b. a warmer liquid.
     c. a faster current.
     d. a current that has more salt.
  4. The coast of northern Europe is warmer because
     a. it receives warmer air from the south.
     b. it is naturally warm.
     c. the Gulf Stream brings warm air to the coast.
     d. more people live here.

II. STUDY THE INVESTIGATION ON PAGE 57. RELATE WHAT HAPPENS HERE TO WHAT HAPPENS IN THE FORMATION OF OCEAN CURRENTS.

III. FIND THE EXPLANATION. IN WHICH SECTION OF THE CHAPTER IS THE ANSWER TO EACH OF THE FOLLOWING QUESTIONS? WRITE THE QUESTION AND THE ANSWER IN YOUR NOTEBOOK.

1. Why are icebergs found in the shipping lanes far to the south?
2. Why do waters near the equator move toward the poles?
3. How can we chart an ocean current?
4. Why does England have thick fogs?

IV. TRUE OR FALSE? IF THE STATEMENT IS TRUE, WRITE TRUE. IF THE STATEMENT IS FALSE, CHANGE THE WORDS IN ITALICS TO MAKE THE STATEMENT TRUE.

1. Thor Heyerdahl's trip proved that the migration of man was controlled by *tides.*
2. To obtain the speed of a current we use an instrument known as the *drift bottle.*
3. The Sargasso Sea is part of the *Labrador Current.*
4. The man who first measured the temperature of the Gulf Stream was *Jacques Piccard.*
5. The clockwise movement of water in the North Atlantic is caused by the *tides.*

V. GETTING IT STRAIGHT.

Which of the groups of ocean currents is all warm?
a. Japan, Brazil, Peru.
b. Labrador, Japan, Brazil.
c. Gulf, Japan, Brazil.
d. Gulf, Japan, North Atlantic.

CHAPTER 8

Waves:
Powerhouses
of the Sea

PROBLEM:
What do we know
about the causes and
nature of waves?

8–1 SURFING AT THE SHORE

It's fun to glide over the waves at top speed with only a flat piece of wood between your feet and the water. This is the popular sport called *surfing*. The surfer paddles out to where the waves start breaking and proceeds to ride them. The trick is to keep the board just ahead of the wave top. For the greatest speed, the wave should be just on the point of breaking.

What is it about a powerful wave that gives the surfer his ride? Let's study the causes and movements of the waves.

FIG. 65–1. What does a surfer have to know about the movements of waves?

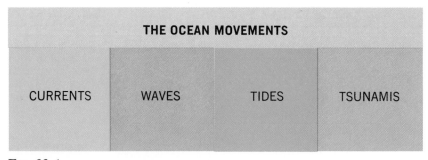

THE OCEAN MOVEMENTS

CURRENTS   WAVES   TIDES   TSUNAMIS

Fɪɢ. 66–1.

8–2 WHAT IS A WAVE?

Visit a pier or dock on a windy day. If possible, bring a pair of binoculars with you. Look at some of the waves. All waves have some common features. The top of the wave is called the *CREST* (KREST). The low point is known as the *TROUGH* (TRAWF). The height of the wave is the distance between the crest and the trough. See if you can find these points. If the day is windy, you may see waves of different shapes and sizes.

If we had a special camera with which to look into a wave, we would find that each particle of water moves in a circular pattern called an *ELLIPSE* (ee-LIPS). Let's use a piece of rope to describe this action. Tie a piece of rope (about 15 feet long) to a door handle. Shake the free end of the rope up and down. A wave will be formed along the rope. The wave moves along the rope, but the rope is still attached to the door handle.

Water waves are like rope waves. It is the wave that moves, not the water. As the wave moves along, the water particles move in a circular fashion. One way to observe this is to watch a boat bobbing on the waves. The boat is actually lifted toward the crest. Once over the top, it appears to slide down the trough. When the wave has passed, the boat will not have moved very far.

8–3 CAUSES OF WAVES

How are waves started? Most ocean waves are produced by winds. As the wind blows against the surface of the water, the water begins to rise and fall. This is a regular movement, as in the rope experiment.

How can the rope show bigger waves? You are right! Apply more energy. It is the same for ocean waves.

Strong (East) Winds	Form	Longer Waves and Higher Waves	Than	Weak (Slow) Winds

What other factors control the size of waves? Examine the chart below.

These Control the Size of the Wave		
Speed of the Wind	Length of Time Wind Blows	Distance Over Which It Travels

Waves in the Atlantic reach about 40 feet in height; Pacific waves rise to about 50 feet. In big storms, waves may rise to 100 feet. One of the largest waves ever seen was reported in the Pacific at 112 feet!

8–4 THE FORM OF A WAVE

Look back into Section 7–3. Now examine Figure 67–1 below. As you can see, the length of the wave is measured from crest to crest. The height is measured from crest to trough.

FIG. 67–1. Length and height are important wave measurements. Can you think of a third measurement?

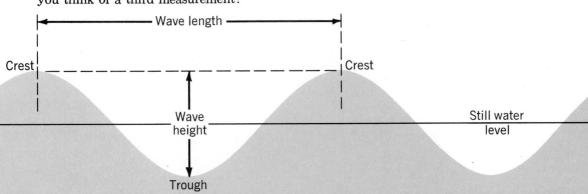

8–5 WHITECAPS AND FOAM

If you're ever near the ocean on a windy day, look out over the water for *WHITECAPS*. These are powerful, wind-driven waves. They start breaking before they reach the shore. When the wind force is more than 12 miles per hour, some of the smaller waves grow. The height of the wave is greater than its length. The crest moves faster than the main body and it topples over.

What do you think the whitecap is caused by? If you said "foam," you are right. Foam is made of air bubbles that bounce off one another. It's similar to a roomful of balloons hitting one another.

LEARNED SO FAR

- Waves are rhythmic movements of water in the ocean.
- Waves are caused by winds.
- Strength and speed of waves depend on strength, speed, and distance of the winds.
- In waves, the wave energy moves, the water does not.

8–6 AT THE SHORE

On a windy day, you can see the way waves break on the beach. When the wave leaves deeper water, it undergoes changes. Churned up by the winds, it has stored a great deal

FIG. 68–1. Past the breakers, a body or ship moves only up or down. What does this prove?

of energy. When the wave reaches shallow water, this energy is released. As the wave comes near the shore, the lower part drags at the bottom; it is slowed. But the top part of the wave keeps going at the same speed. Thus, it "rolls over" and crashes onto the shore. These crashing waves are called *BREAKERS*. Look for the *SPILLING* breakers; they fall on shores with a gentle slope. One way to recognize them is to look for a long line of foam tumbling down the front. These are the waves that surfers love to ride. Where the bottom rises very steeply, as on rocky coasts, waves hit rocks with loud booms. These are known as *PLUNGING* breakers.

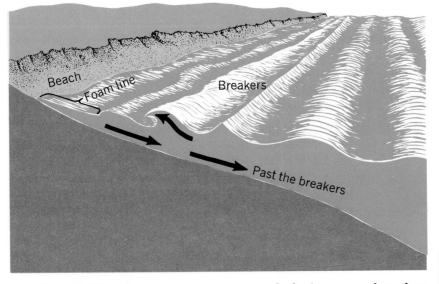

FIG. 69–1. Spilling breakers release a great deal of energy when they hit the shore. On what type of coastline would you find this type of wave?

8–7 LONGSHORE AND RIP CURRENTS

Do you know why lifeguards permit swimming only in certain areas? Why they blow their whistles when you swim out too far? As waves break along the beach, a lot of water accumulates near the land. Since the incoming breakers prevent the water from moving out again, it travels along the shoreline. It is now called a *LONGSHORE CURRENT*. The water heads out to sea again wherever the incoming waves are weaker. In this area, it is called a *RIP CURRENT* or *UNDERTOW*. A swimmer caught in this current can be swept out to sea.

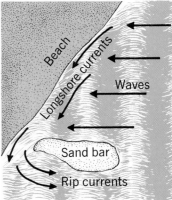

FIG. 69–2.
Why do you think a rip current is commonly called an "undertow"?

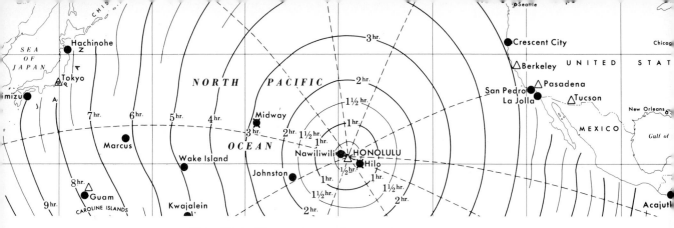

FIG. 70-1. Tsunami warning service operated by the U.S. Coast and Geodetic Service. Why is it important that people know the estimated time of arrival of the huge waves?

8–8 GIANTS OF THE SEA

The Japanese have a word for it: *TSUNAMI* (tsoo-NOM-ee). Not all waves are caused by winds. Some arise when an undersea earthquake "acts up." Such a quake forms a huge crack or *FAULT* on the sea bottom. Water then rushes into the crack, causing waves to form on the surface. These tsunamis may produce only three or four waves. But when they approach the shore they rise very high. They also travel very far, possibly as much as 2,000 miles. Tsunami waves sometimes extend almost 100 miles from crest to crest.

The waves that hit Hawaii in 1946 killed 173 people and destroyed $25 million worth of property. After this disaster, a warning service was set up in the Pacific Ocean. By estimating the speed and time of arrival, this service can give people on land time to move to safer areas. Since tsunamis are caused by earthquakes, the most useful instrument in this service is the *SEISMOGRAPH* (SIZ-muh-graf).

FIG. 70-2. Tsunami's damage in Alaska. How do tsunamis differ from regular waves? How can they be predicted?

● Crashing waves are called breakers.
● Spilling breakers fall on shorelines that have a gentle slope; plunging breakers are found on rocky coastlines.
● Longshore currents move along the shore; a rip current or undertow heads out to sea again, where the waves are weaker.
● Tsunamis are caused by undersea earthquakes.

Self-Study Guide for Chapter 8

I. KNOWING AND UNDERSTANDING. FIND THE ANSWER. WRITE IT IN YOUR NOTEBOOK.

1. When a wave mass moves along, the water particles
   a. stay in one place.
   b. move in an ellipse.
   c. move to the side.
   d. move down below the wave.
2. The size of a wave is controlled by factors such as
   a. temperature.
   b. color of water.
   c. speed of wind.
   d. cloud cover.
3. Rip currents are caused by
   a. water moving in from the sea.
   b. water moving out to sea.
   c. the movement of waves toward shore.
   d. water being pulled to the bottom.
4. When large sections of the sea floor drop,
   a. continents move into the crack.
   b. water rushes in.
   c. wind-generated waves are produced.
   d. rip currents are formed.

II. FIND THE EXPLANATION. IN WHICH SECTION OF THE CHAPTER IS THE ANSWER TO EACH OF THE FOLLOWING QUESTIONS? WRITE THE QUESTION AND THE ANSWER IN YOUR NOTEBOOK.

1. How can observations of a boat demonstrate that it is the wave shape rather then the water itself that moves?
2. Why are longshore currents formed?
3. What can happen when a portion of the sea floor caves in?
4. What causes a wave?

III. STUDY THE DIAGRAM IN FIGURE 67–1. CHOOSE THE WORD THAT BEST APPLIES TO EACH QUESTION. WRITE IN YOUR NOTEBOOK.

1. What do we call the top of a wave?
2. How is the length of a wave measured?
3. The height of a wave is measured from _____ to _____.

IV. CAUSES AND EFFECTS. IN THE LISTS BELOW, ONE GIVES CAUSES AND THE OTHER EFFECTS. MATCH THE CORRECT CAUSE AND EFFECT IN YOUR NOTEBOOK.

Causes	*Effects*
1. Faulting of the sea bed	a. Breaker
2. Waves approaching shallow water	b. Erosion
	c. Tsunami
3. Waves hitting a rocky coast	d. Undertow
4. Current moving away from beach	e. Tsunami warning service
5. Hawaiian waves of 1946	f. Plunging breakers

V. GO AND DISCOVER

Visit a beach at low tide and make a study of any erosion going on. Is there any indication that the waves and currents are sweeping away the sands? Look for an area where beach grasses are growing. Is there less erosion here?

VI. STATE THE DIFFERENCE CLEARLY IN YOUR OWN WORDS.

1. What is the difference between ripples and waves?
2. What is the difference between an undertow and a breaker?
3. What is the difference between a bar and a causeway?

CHAPTER 9   Tides: The Rise and Fall of Ocean Water

PROBLEM:
What are the causes and the rhythms of tides?

9–1 HIGH WATER, LOW WATER

The class arrived at the beach, spread their blankets, and prepared for a day of fun. After spending an hour in the water, they decided to return to the blankets to lie in the sun. To their surprise, they found their blankets almost covered by the rising water. What caused this rapid movement of water onto the shore? The students in our story learned about tides the "wet" way. Could they have timed it? Could they have predicted it?

When the students arrived at the beach they made the mistake of spreading the blankets too close to the water's edge. At that time the water level was at its low point or *EBB*. When the water rose over the blankets it reached its high or *FLOOD* level. We call this rise and fall of ocean water the *TIDES*. The distance the tide traveled between its lowest and highest points is called the *TIDAL RANGE*. In certain parts of the world, the range may be 60 feet above low tide.

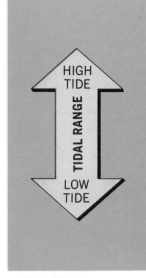

Fig. 73–1.

73

The rise and fall of tides from the ebb to the flood has been known from ancient times. Long ago, as man watched the oceans, he found that there was a *regular* time or *rhythm* in these changes. By careful observation, he could time them and predict them.

What kind of timing was observed? First, a *daily* change was noticed. There were *two* high tides *every day;* there were *two* low tides *every day.*

But that's not all. It was also soon discovered that there were two specially high tides each *month* and two specially low tides each *month.*

Finally, careful observation showed that the timetable for tides was very much like the timetable for the changes or *PHASES* (FAY-ziz) in the light patterns of the moon.

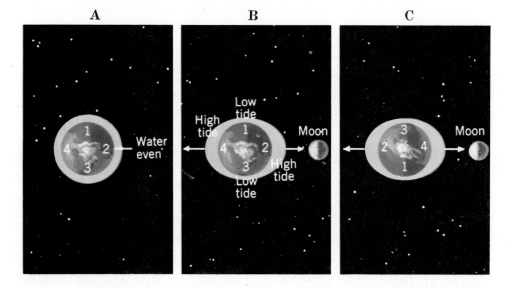

FIG. 74–1.

A. If there were no gravity pull of the moon, the water would be evenly distributed all around the earth.

B. The moon pulls on the earth at point 2. The water rises to high tide at point 2. The water on the opposite side also rises as the earth is pulled away from it. At points 1 and 3, the water falls for a low tide.

C. Exactly 6 hours and 13 minutes later, the earth has rotated under its waters. Points 1, 2, 3, 4 are in new positions. Points 2 and 4 had low tides. Now, 12 hours and 26 minutes later, points 2 and 4 have their second high tide.

9–3 WHAT CAUSES THE DAILY TIDES?

Let's imagine that we are observing the earth from outer space. Our mission is to watch the movements of the moon and sun and how they affect the oceans. The side of the earth that is closer to the moon "feels the pull" of the moon's gravity more. As a result, the ocean water on the side of the earth facing the moon bulges. A bulge also develops on the opposite side. At any one time, there are two high tides and two low tides.

As the earth spins (rotates), the water tends to "jump off." The pull of the earth—gravity—"holds" the water on.

At the same time, the moon's gravity pulls the water. The moon rises 52 minutes later each day. Thus, every 24 hours and 52 minutes there are two high tides and two lows. This is the actual length of the moon's day. Each day, the tides are about 52 minutes later.

9–4 WHAT DO TIDE TABLES SHOW US?

Tide tables show high tide and low tide. Since we know the schedule of the moon's revolution around the earth, these tables can be set up far in advance.

The numbers in the left-hand column show the days of the month. Using a card or ruler under the line, read across. This will show the correct time for high tides in six nearby places. How can you estimate low tide for any day?

FIG. 75–1. A newspaper tide table.

High Tides Around New York

	Sandy Hook Rockaway Inlet		Willets Point		Shinnecock Canal		Fire Island Inlet		Montauk Point		New London	
	A.M.	P.M.	A.M.	P.M.	A.M.	P.M.	A.M.	P.M.	A.M.	P.M.	A.M.	P.M.
Dec. 22..	1:18	1:34	4:34	4:56	5:58	6:11	0:40	12:56	2:12	2:26	3:25	3:38
Dec. 23..	2:11	2:34	5:27	5:53	6:47	7:06	1:33	1:56	3:01	3:20	4:14	4:33
Dec. 24..	3:11	3:35	6:24	6:53	7:33	8:00	2:33	2:57	3:47	4:14	5:00	5:27
Dec. 25..	4:09	4:39	7:20	7:57	8:18	8:51	3:31	4:01	4:32	5:05	5:45	6:18
Dec. 26..	5:05	5:35	8:15	8:53	9:04	9:38	4:27	4:57	5:18	5:52	6:31	7:05
Dec. 27..	5:55	6:24	9:08	9:48	9:50	10:25	5:17	5:46	6:04	6:39	7:17	7:52

For high tide at Jones Inlet (Pt. Lookout), deduct 19 min. from Sandy Hook time.
For high tide at Atlantic City (Steel Pier), deduct 26 min. from Sandy Hook time.

- Tides are the rhythmic rise and fall of ocean water.
- There are daily high tides and low tides; there are monthly high tides and low tides.
- Tides are caused mainly by the pull of the moon. Every 24 hours and 52 minutes, there are two high tides and two low tides.
- Tides may be predicted on convenient tables.

9–5   THE MOON'S HELPER—THE SUN

As we said before, there are unusually high and unusually low tides at certain times of the month.

Farther out in space, the sun also pulls on the earth's waters by its gravity. Is this pull stronger than the moon's or weaker? Although the sun is very much larger, the moon is nearer the earth. Therefore, the pull of the moon is more than twice as strong. Let's see how this works.

9–6   DOUBLE PULL: SPRING TIDES

When the sun and moon are in a direct line, the tidal range is high. At this time, there are very high tides and very low tides. They are called *SPRING TIDES*. They come twice a month: at full moon (full face) and new moon (face not visible).

FIG. 76–1. Spring tides are produced when the sun and moon are in a direct line. Why are there such high tides?

9-7 RIGHT-ANGLE PULL: NEAP TIDES

When the moon and sun are at right angles, they work against each other. This happens when the moon is in its first and last quarters. Now the tides are not quite so high nor quite so low. We call these *NEAP TIDES* (NEEP). This also happens twice during the month.

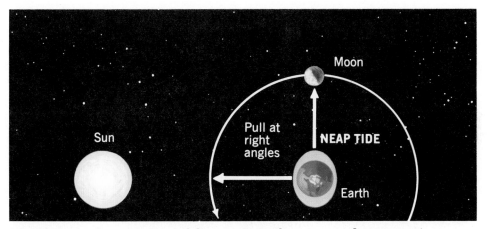

FIG. 77–1. At first quarter and last quarter, the moon and sun are at right angles. The face of the sun and the face of the moon work against each other. Now the tides are not quite so high and not quite so low. This is the neap tide.

FIG. 77–2. Low tide along the Bay of Fundy, Canada. What causes this movement of water?

9-8 DEPENDS ON WHERE YOU LIVE

A friend of yours lives 20 miles south of your town. The time of high tide on his table is 10 minutes earlier than yours. Why do we find such differences? We must remember that coastlines are *not straight*. Adding to this is the *roughness* of the ocean bottom. This slows the waters down and results in differences in tides.

In the Bay of Fundy, near New Brunswick, Canada, a narrow channel changes the shape of the incoming tide. The water has a steep front as it moves upstream. This is called a *TIDAL BORE*.

9-9 TIDES AND OUR ACTIVITIES

We watch the tides to time our sailings. Tugboat captains examine the tide tables to begin pulling giant freighters out of the shallow harbors. Are you going fishing? Then you will watch the tides to find the kind you want. Tides are surely important in our lives.

LEARNED SO FAR

SUMMARY OF TIDES

Daily tides	High Low High Low	6 hours, 13 minutes between each
Spring tides (2 each month)	Full moon New moon	About 14 days apart
Neap tides (2 each month)	First quarter Last quarter	About 14 days apart

Self-Study Guide for Chapter 9

I. KNOWING AND UNDERSTANDING. FIND THE ANSWER. WRITE IT IN YOUR NOTEBOOK.

1. High tides come 52 minutes later each day because
   a. the sun and moon pull at the same time.
   b. of a friction against the earth's surface.
   c. the sun interferes.
   d. the moon rises 52 minutes later each day.

2. When it is low tide on our side of the world, the side opposite us has
   a. a spring tide.
   b. a low tide.
   c. a high tide.
   d. a flood tide.

3. Spring tides
   a. are stronger than neap tides.
   b. are caused by bores.
   c. come with every spring.
   d. are not related to gravity.

4. A neap tide is formed when
   a. the moon and sun form a straight line.
   b. the waves are high.
   c. the weather is cold.
   d. the moon is at right angles to the sun.

II. FIND THE EXPLANATION. IN WHICH SECTION OF THE CHAP-
TER IS THE ANSWER TO EACH OF THE FOLLOWING QUES-
TIONS? WRITE THE QUESTION AND THE ANSWER IN YOUR
NOTEBOOK.

1. Why are there two high and two low tides each day?
2. Why do we have different tide schedules for the same part of
the world?
3. What causes the spring tide?
4. What causes the neap tide?

III. NUMBER, PLEASE. WRITE THE WHOLE SENTENCE IN YOUR
NOTEBOOK.

1. Each tide lasts about _____ hours and _____ minutes.
2. Each high tide comes about _____ minutes later each day.
3. The length of a moon or lunar day is _____.
4. Every month there are _____ spring tides.

IV. WHAT'S THE DIFFERENCE? COMPARE THE WORDS. STATE
THE DIFFERENCE BETWEEN WORDS IN EACH PAIR.

1. Flood tide—ebb tide.
2. Tidal range—tidal bore.
3. Neap tide—spring tide.

V. ROUNDING OUT YOUR KNOWLEDGE.

1. What is meant by tideland?
2. What are tide pools?
3. How are tidelands and tide pools important for marine life?

CHAPTER 10

The Chemistry of Seawater

PROBLEM:
*What are the
chemical and physical
characteristics of
ocean water?*

10-1 HOW SHALL WE DESCRIBE OCEAN WATER?

We have talked about the forces and motions of the water. We can also study its composition—its *chemistry*. The *physics* of ocean water involves the study of other natural forces such as temperature, pressure, light, and sound.

These things are important to us because ocean water affects ocean life. The study of plants and animals in relation to their environment is called *ECOLOGY* (ee-KOL-uh-jee).

A knowledge of ocean water also helps us design ships, bridges, and underwater cables. It helps us find ways to choose and preserve the materials we use.

If we know about ocean water, we can plan to make good use of the oceans in the future.

10-2 WHY IS THE OCEAN SALTY?

The oceans are water, H_2O, but not "pure" water. Where does the salt come from?

As we saw in Chapter 5, rivers carry minerals from the land to the sea. The ocean is, therefore, a "catch-all" basin for land materials. So the ocean is a *solution*. Other materials are *dissolved* in it and are invisible.

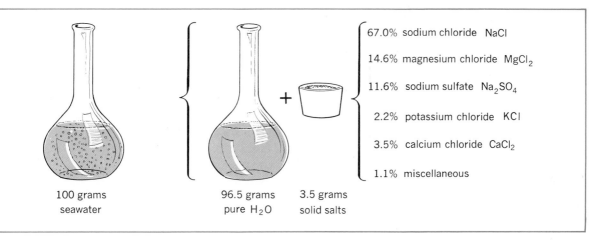

100 grams
seawater

96.5 grams
pure H$_2$O

3.5 grams
solid salts

67.0% sodium chloride NaCl

14.6% magnesium chloride MgCl$_2$

11.6% sodium sulfate Na$_2$SO$_4$

2.2% potassium chloride KCl

3.5% calcium chloride CaCl$_2$

1.1% miscellaneous

FIG. 81–1. The solid part taken from ocean water contains many compounds. Look up the word *salt* in a good chemistry book. What kind of element is found in every salt?

Was the ocean always salty? There is a theory that millions of years ago, the ocean water was "fresh" or nonsalty. We also know that the ocean grows saltier at a steady rate as time goes by.

The chief mineral or compound in the sea is common table salt. This is *SODIUM CHLORIDE*, a compound of sodium and chlorine. The chemical formula is NaCl. How much of the water is NaCl? Look at Figure 81–1 above.

10–3 OTHER SALTS: HOW MUCH?

The amount of dissolved salts in water is called its *SALINITY* (suh-LIN-uh-tee).

From careful experiments, scientists know that dissolved chemicals make up 35 parts per 1,000 of seawater. Look at the percentages in Figure 81–1. Sodium chloride is the most abundant. The other salts are found in only small amounts. Another way to say this is that the *average* salinity of the ocean is 3½ percent.

INVESTIGATION: How can we identify some common salts in ocean water?

PROCEDURES

1. Moisten solid sodium chloride with a drop of hydrochloric acid. Pick up some of the moistened crystals on a nichrome wire loop. Hold the loop in a Bunsen flame.
2. Repeat with calcium and with potassium.
3. Repeat these tests with seawater.

OBSERVATIONS AND ANALYSIS

1. What colors result from each pure chemical?
2. What colors result from seawater?
3. Can this experiment tell you about quantities? Explain.

LEARNED SO FAR

● We study the characteristics of ocean water to understand marine ecology, to solve marine engineering problems, to remove useful products from the ocean.
● Ocean minerals are brought from the land by rivers.
● Salinity refers to the amount of dissolved salts in the sea. Seawater is 3½ percent salt.

10–4   SALINITY AND THE WEIGHT OF SEAWATER

How do dissolved salts change the "weight" of seawater?

FIG. 82–1.

FRESH WATER   SALT WATER

DO AND DISCOVER

INVESTIGATION: How do you measure the salinity of seawater?

PROCEDURES

1. Get two lead pencils with erasers. Stick a thumbtack into the eraser end of each pencil. The tack will act as the weight to hold the pencil in the water.

2. Fill a one-quart bottle with tap (sink) water. Float the pencil in the water. Observe the level to which it sinks. Mark it off with a notch.
3. Fill a second bottle with seawater or a very concentrated salt solution. Observe the level to which the pencil sinks. Mark it off.

OBSERVATIONS AND ANALYSIS

1. In which liquid did the pencil float higher? Explain.
2. Which water is "heavier," tap water or salt water?

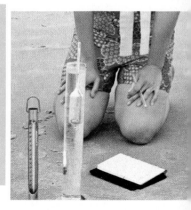

FIG. 83–1.
How can the hydrometer above be used to see which water has more salt?

Because of the dissolved minerals, seawater is "heavier" than fresh water. To put it another way, the *DENSITY* (DEN-suh-tee) of the water has increased. To measure the higher density of the water, we use an instrument known as a *HY-DROMETER* (hy-DROM-uh-tur). A hydrometer is a hollow glass tube that is weighted at one end so that the tube will float upright. Hydrometers sink less in seawater than in fresh water. Can you explain why?

FIG. 83–2.
A hydrometer.

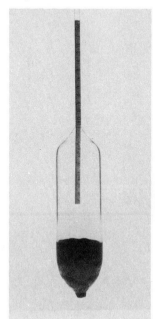

10–5 DISSOLVED GASES IN THE SEA

So far, we have mentioned the solids dissolved in the sea. Chemical tests show that the ocean also contains dissolved gases. What are these gases? Where do they come from?

All gases in the atmosphere are also dissolved in ocean water. The two chief gases are carbon dioxide (CO_2) and oxygen (O_2). These gases are found in greater amounts at the surface than at deeper levels.

Some of these gases are simply dissolved from the atmosphere into the ocean's surface. Rain, falling into the ocean, brings large amounts of these gases into the sea.

Floating green plants in the sea produce oxygen during the process of *PHOTOSYNTHESIS* (fo-tuh-SIN-thuh-sis). This will be discussed in a later chapter.

FIG. 84–1.
The gulf waters near Eilat, Israel, has a high salinity. Why are salinities higher in this part of the world?

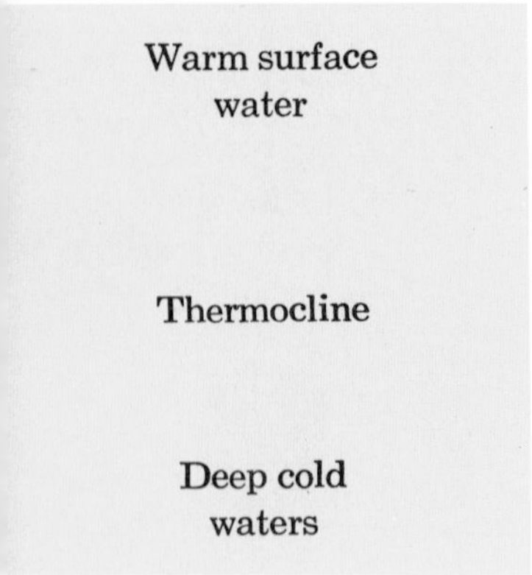

Warm surface water

Thermocline

Deep cold waters

FIG. 84–2.

10–6 DIFFERENCES IN SALINITY

Everyone can float in the Dead Sea in Israel! Everyone can float in the Great Salt Lake in Utah! As you can guess, this can be explained by salinity.

If you wanted to find the salinities of the world's oceans, you would first have to collect samples and test them with a hydrometer. An average of the different readings would fall between 34 and 37 parts per 1,000. But in the warmer parts of the world (tropics), readings may be as high as 40 parts per 1,000. Why such high salinities?

Take a jar of salt water and heat it gently. The water will begin to *EVAPORATE* (ee-VAP-uh-rate). But the salt remains in the bottle. The same thing happens in the ocean. Warm climates speed up evaporation, which leaves salt behind. As a result, the density of the water increases. In the tropics, for example, air temperatures can exceed 100 degrees, causing a very high evaporation rate. Salinities can get very high. Near the poles, evaporation is lower; therefore salinity is lower.

High rainfall and a source of fresh water can lower the salinity. This occurs along the coasts wherever rivers enter the sea. Water with a lowered salinity is called *BRACKISH* (BRAK-ish). In addition, melting icebergs and snow bring fresh water into the ocean. This also reduces salinity.

10–7 TEMPERATURES OF THE OCEAN

Try diving into a lake or bay. When you are near the bottom, the water may be a little cooler. What is the reason for this temperature difference? The warmer region of any body of water is always near the surface. As we move to the depths below, sunlight does not penetrate. It is much colder there. Warmer water is lighter and floats on top. Colder water is heavier and sinks. The point between warm and cold regions is known as the *THERMOCLINE* (THUR-mo-kline).

Look at Figure 85–1. You will see that the North and South Poles have temperatures well below the freezing point of water. If salt lowers the freezing point of water, why do we find ice floes in this part of the world? The ice above is actually made up of water that has evaporated from the seawater below and has very little salt. Below this ice, the water is not frozen.

SAMPLE TEMPERATURES OF THE OCEAN

Equator and tropics	86°F
North and South Poles	28°F
Red Sea	90°F
Indian Ocean	80°F
Atlantic Ocean near New York (winter)	55°F
Atlantic Ocean near New York (summer)	65°F

FIG. 85–1. Ocean temperatures differ in many parts of the world. Why is the water warmer near the tropics?

10–8 LIGHT IN OCEAN WATERS

Ocean water is *transparent*. It allows light to go through it. The light that enters the ocean is made up of various colors. We can easily see this if we pass sunlight through a *PRISM* (PRIZ-um). The light is broken down into the colors of the *SPECTRUM* (SPEK-trum). The red end of the spectrum is made up of long waves, while the blue and violet ends are made up of shorter waves. Long waves of light are absorbed by the surface waters. Shorter-wave light—such as green, blue, and violet—penetrates to greater depths.

How far does light go down into the ocean? The chart below shows that light reaches about 600 feet below the surface. The brightest light is near the top. There is no light below 600 feet.

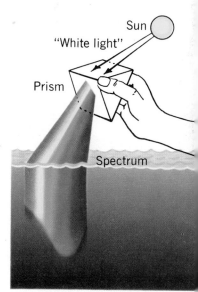

FIG. 85–2. Light is made up of many colors. What colors make up the spectrum?

LIGHT ZONES IN OCEANS

Surface to 250 feet	Good light for plant growth
250 feet to 600 feet	Dim light—no green plant growth
600 feet to sea bottom	Darkness—no plants

10–9 THE COLOR OF OCEAN WATER

Light also gives the ocean its color. Actually, the water itself has no color. The color is due to the reflection of sunlight by the sky or by the dissolved minerals. Thus, the Red Sea is not red; the Yellow Sea is not yellow; the Black Sea is not black.

LEARNED SO FAR

- Seawater is heavier than fresh water because of its dissolved salts.
- The chief gases in the sea are CO_2 and O_2.
- Warmer waters have a higher salinity than colder waters.
- Cold water is much heavier than warm water.
- Ocean water is transparent and allows light to penetrate it.

Self-Study Guide for Chapter 10

I. KNOWING AND UNDERSTANDING. FIND THE ANSWER. WRITE IT IN YOUR NOTEBOOK.

1. The ocean became salty because
   a. rainwater contains salts.
   b. salts come from bottom sediments.
   c. salts were washed from the land by rivers.
   d. salts were always present in the oceans.
2. If salts were added to fresh water, the salinity
   a. would increase.
   b. would decrease.
   c. would not be affected.
   d. would cause the temperature to change.
3. A hydrometer would tend to float higher in a solution with
   a. low salinity.
   b. fresh water.
   c. high salinity.
   d. much dissolved oxygen.

II. FIND THE EXPLANATION. IN WHICH SECTION OF THE CHAP-
TER IS THE ANSWER TO EACH OF THE FOLLOWING QUES-
TIONS? WRITE THE QUESTION AND THE ANSWER IN YOUR
NOTEBOOK.

    1. Why is seawater heavier than fresh water?
    2. Why do you find colder water near the ocean bottom?
    3. How does the nature of ocean water help us to understand
       ecology?
    4. How far does light go down into the ocean?

III. ON THE LADDER OF UNDERSTANDING. WRITE THE FOLLOW-
ING STATEMENTS IN YOUR NOTEBOOK. CHOOSE THE COR-
RECT NUMBER OR PHRASE FROM THE PARENTHESES TO
COMPLETE THE SENTENCE.

    1. The average salinity of seawater is about (20, 35, 10) parts per
       1,000.
    2. A (thermometer, hydrometer, barometer) is used to measure
       the salinity of seawater.
    3. Warmer water is (heavier, wetter, lighter) than cold water.
    4. In warmer parts of the oceans, salinities are (higher, lower)
       than they are in temperate parts.
    5. Salt (lowers, raises) the freezing point of water.
    6. The red end of the light spectrum is made up of (long, short)
       waves.

IV. VISIT YOUR LOCAL GAS STATION.

Ask the attendant to show you how he uses a hydrometer. Prepare
a report for your class.

V. TRY IT YOURSELF—HOME EXPERIMENT.

Measure the salinity of seawater before and after it has been kept
in a warm place for several hours. What do you find? Explain your
answer.

VI. PUT ON YOUR THINKING CAP.

    1. Are the oceans less salty or more salty near areas of much rain-
       fall? Explain your answer.
    2. Why is the Red Sea far more salty (40 percent) than average
       ocean water?

UNIT III   Marine Biology: Life in the Sea

WHAT'S IT ALL ABOUT?

Plants and animals, whether on land or in the sea, live *together*. The stress is on the word *together*. Why? Because living things depend on each other for nutrition, their responses, their reproduction—yes, their very lives.

Living things also depend on their surroundings or *ENVIRONMENT* . . . *all* factors of their environment: food, water, oxygen, minerals, pressure, and temperature all affect living things.

As we saw before, a very important branch of science is *ECOLOGY*—the study of the *togetherness of life*.

In this unit, we shall study those living things whose environment is in or near the ocean. This subject is *MARINE BIOLOGY*. We shall first talk about the ecological factors that affect life in the sea. Then we shall survey the wonderful world of marine life. You will find it a fascinating story . . . a story that may solve some of man's greatest problems.

CHAPTER 11

Marine Ecology

PROBLEM:
How does the marine environment affect living things?

FIG. 90–1.
Crown-of-thorns starfish.

FIG. 90–2.
Charles Darwin.

11–1 THE CROWN-OF-THORNS PROBLEM

Moving slowly along the Pacific reefs, a crown-of-thorns starfish slowly begins to eat away at the coral heads—destroying the reef in its path. If nothing is done to stop it, the lovely coral reefs of the Pacific will be destroyed forever.

What can be done to stop this destruction? Shall we dump chemicals into the water to kill the starfish? Shall we try electric shock? Shall we simply collect all the starfish we can? One moment of thought, and you will conclude that none of these is acceptable.

Living things have a relationship with the factors of their environment. But don't they also relate to other living things around them? Couldn't we find some natural enemy of the crown-of-thorns starfish?

We shall get back to this question after we explore the subject of this chapter: *marine ecology*.

11–2 SURVIVAL OF THE FITTEST

How are living things affected by other living things?

Have you ever heard the phrase *struggle for existence*? This colorful phrase was used by the biologist *Charles Darwin* to describe the competition among living things. What do they compete for? For food, for space, for oxygen, for mates! According to biologists, those organisms that are better adapted to their environment win out. Darwin called this the *survival of the fittest.*

11–3 BALANCE AND CONTROL

The organisms of the sea stay "in balance," so that one population in the environment does not outstrip another. How? The chart below gives you this answer.

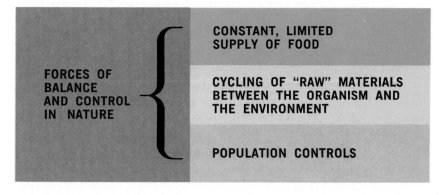

FORCES OF
BALANCE
AND CONTROL
IN NATURE

CONSTANT, LIMITED
SUPPLY OF FOOD

CYCLING OF "RAW" MATERIALS
BETWEEN THE ORGANISM AND
THE ENVIRONMENT

POPULATION CONTROLS

Fig. 91–1.

If the population becomes too large, the food supply will tend to run out. This will result in fighting, and only the strong and able organisms will be able to capture food. Overcrowding is then a limiting factor.

Every animal group has its enemies. The animal that attacks is known as the *PREDATOR* (PRED-uh-tor). The one that is eaten is called the *PREY* (PRAY). The predator-prey relationship is nature's way of controlling animal populations so that overcrowding does not take place.

Think back to the crown-of-thorns problem. Who is the predator? Who is the prey? Do you now see a possible solution? It was soon discovered that the crown-of-thorns did have a natural enemy—the beautiful shellfish *TRITON* (TRY-tun). Perhaps tritons were dying for some special reason; perhaps they were being collected for their beautiful shells. As they decreased in numbers, the crown-of-thorns increased and the reefs were attacked. Now, by bringing in tritons and protecting them, the crown-of-thorns will be kept in check. The reef may be saved after all!

- Marine ecology is the branch of oceanography that studies the relationships of living to nonliving and living to living things.
- Those organisms that are better adapted to their environment survive.
- Organisms stay in balance; therefore, populations in the environment do not outstrip one another.

11–4 NONLIVING FACTORS IN THE ENVIRONMENT

We have already seen that the survival of all living things depends on all other living things in the environment. These are the *BIOTIC* (by-OT-ik) factors (*bio* = "life"). In addition, all organisms depend on the raw materials and other factors of the environment. These are the *ABIOTIC* (AY-by-ot-ik) (*a* = "without").

The chart below shows the abiotic factors with which organisms must cope.

FIG. 92–1.

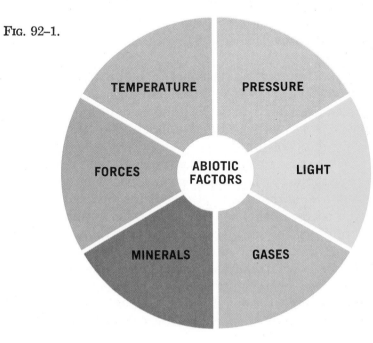

11–5 THE INFLUENCE OF LIGHT

Plants and animals that live in the sea are influenced by the amount of light reaching them. Green plants need light to make their own food. We would then find plants in areas where light can reach them. We shall come back to the food-making process in a later chapter. Green seaweeds cannot use green light; they are found near the surface where they can absorb the longer waves, such as red and orange. Red seaweeds absorb the green and blue wavelengths and hence are found at greater depths.

Are animals affected by light? Indirectly, their food supply depends on green plants. But light also affects the appearance of marine animals. Did you know that the color of fish depends on the level of the ocean at which they live?

Light also affects the movements of certain marine animals. Many animals travel between the surface and the depths below when light changes occur. Finally, light affects the behavior of marine animals. Look at Figure 93–1 above.

FIG. 93–1.
Fiddler crabs change color twice a day: at sunrise, they are dark; at sundown, they are pale. This crab gets its name from its large, fiddlelike front claw.

DO AND DISCOVER

INVESTIGATION: How does light affect animals?

PROCEDURES
1. Obtain a quart milk bottle and cover it with black construction paper. Hold the paper in place with rubber bands.
2. The live specimens used will depend on where you live. Many pet shops sell an organism known as *DAPHNIA* (DAF-nee-uh) for fish food. If you live near a pond you can also catch your own Daphnia (or use brine shrimp).
3. Fill the bottle with fresh water and add about 30 Daphnia. Make sure they are swimming in all directions.
4. Shine a flashlight on the surface for 10 minutes.
5. Remove the black paper and observe.
6. Try the experiment without the light.

OBSERVATIONS AND ANALYSIS
1. Are the animals attracted to the light?
2. Daphnia live in freshwater ponds. Give some reasons why you feel they react to light in this manner.

FIG. 93–2.
Daphnia.

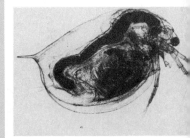

When the weather turns colder, birds prepare for their journey to warmer climates. This is called *MIGRATION* (my-GRAY-shun). Ocean temperatures have the same effect on many marine creatures. Bluefish and summer flounder leave our northern bays and inlets for southern waters. Codfish prefer colder water and move toward the shore.

11–6 THE INFLUENCE OF TEMPERATURE

Visit a salt marsh in winter and you will find that a lot of things have changed since the summer. The grasses that grew so well have died. Many of the crabs that were "all over" are deep in their burrows. Many of the small animals are hibernating. Since they are cold-blooded, their body temperatures get lower. This causes them to slow down and go into an extended period of sleep. When warmer weather returns, the marsh will come to life again.

11–7 THE INFLUENCE OF SALINITY

We have already seen that the most plentiful mineral in the sea is sodium chloride. How does salt affect life? Chemists have found that the concentration of salt in ocean water is about the same as that in living matter. Do sea animals have to adapt to salt?

The life story of the salmon is fascinating and illustrates this problem. The young fish are born in freshwater streams. When old enough, they migrate to the sea. Here they will spend a number of years until they are mature adults. They then return to the rivers of their birth to reproduce and die.

Salmon must adapt to both fresh and salt water. But there are many creatures that cannot live in salinities lower than 35 parts per 1,000. Others may be able to survive at very high salinities. Consider what happens to the little animals left behind in the small pools created by the outgoing tide. When these pools are exposed to the sunlight, they heat up rapidly. This causes a high rate of evaporation and a high salinity. Any creature living here must be able to adapt to this change.

Fig. 94–1. Salmon spend their lives in both salt and fresh water. How are they able to live in both environments?

11–8 INFLUENCE OF MINERALS AND GASES

One cycle in the ocean includes the dissolved gases, carbon dioxide, and oxygen. We shall zero in on this cycle when we study food making in green plants (Section 13–4).

Of course, you realize that living things in the ocean die sooner or later. What happens to them? You are right: they *decay*. The *ORGANIC* (or-GAN-ik) or living compounds are broken down. This releases carbon, phosphorus, and nitrogen. These are used by green plants in food making. They are also needed by all creatures to build new living matter.

So you see, cycling is an important process in ocean life.

11–9 THE INFLUENCE OF THE OCEAN'S FORCES

Reviewing quickly, the ocean's forces include currents, waves, and water pressure.

We learned in Chapter 9 that tides cover and uncover our shores twice a day. Marine organisms that live along the coasts must be able to survive this sudden exposure. One thing is certain: they cannot dry out or they will die quickly. They must either dig into the bottom for moisture, hide in wet areas, or move with the outgoing tide. Shore animals have special ways in which they can adapt to this condition. Some have hard shells which they can close up and keep closed until the next tide comes. Others can release a slimy covering which prevents them from drying out.

In the ocean, pressure gets greater with depth. At 33 feet below the surface, the pressure is *twice* that of air. In some deep trenches, pressure is 1,000 times that at sea level. Deep-sea fish have internal pressure to equalize the outer pressure so they are not crushed. Most sea animals stay at their own level. Deep-sea fish are often flat and streamlined to resist water pressure.

FIG. 95–1. Could these animals live on a sandy beach? Why?

- Abiotic factors are the nonliving factors in the environment that influence marine life.
- Marine plants and animals have many ways to adapt to the abiotic factors.

Self-Study Guide for Chapter 11

I. KNOWING AND UNDERSTANDING. FIND THE ANSWER. WRITE IT IN YOUR NOTEBOOK.

   1. "Survival of the fittest" among living organisms means that
      a. the weaker organisms get more food.
      b. the better adapted organisms win out over the weaker ones.
      c. both strong and weak organisms survive.
      d. no weak organisms survive.
   2. If the population becomes too large for the food supply,
      a. the food supply will increase.
      b. the predators will decrease.
      c. food supply will stay the same.
      d. the food supply will decrease.
   3. Green seaweeds cannot live in deep water because
      a. oxygen is not present.
      b. water temperature is too cold.
      c. proper light cannot reach them.
      d. animals would feed on them.
   4. Temperature changes in the ocean may cause animals to
      a. eat more.
      b. become more active.
      c. slow down their bodily activities.
      d. react more to light.

II. FIND THE EXPLANATION. IN WHICH SECTION OF THE CHAPTER IS THE ANSWER TO EACH OF THE FOLLOWING QUESTIONS? WRITE THE QUESTION AND THE ANSWER IN YOUR NOTEBOOK.

   1. What is meant by *natural enemy?*
   2. Why is the predator-prey relationship important in balance?
   3. Why is it important to the salmon to be able to live in both fresh and salt water?

III. ON THE LADDER OF UNDERSTANDING. IN YOUR NOTEBOOK, COMPLETE EACH SENTENCE BY SUPPLYING THE MISSING WORDS.

1. To measure the density of seawater, the scientists use a _____.
2. The point between warm and cold regions is known as the _____.
3. The oxygen found in seawater comes from _____.
4. Tides are caused by the pull of the _____ and moon.
5. Spring tides are caused when the sun and moon are in a _____ line.
6. Large waves that can cause tremendous damage are called _____.
7. Currents in the North Atlantic travel in a _____ direction.
8. Water in a convection current travels from _____ to _____.

IV. STUDY THE INVESTIGATION (PAGE 93). ANSWER THE QUESTIONS BELOW.

1. Why did you place black paper around the sides of the container?
2. Why should the experiment be performed without light?
3. Could other organisms be used? Name some.
4. How can you tell it was not temperature?

V. TRUE OR FALSE? EXPLAIN YOUR ANSWERS.

1. In simple terms, ecology can be described as "the togetherness of life."
2. The "struggle for existence" is also found among plants.
3. The animal that attacks the prey is always the stronger of the two.
4. Abiotic factors are more important than the living factors in the environment.
5. Salmon cannot live in salt water.
6. Green seaweeds are found at greater depths because they can use the green and blue wavelengths.

VI. READ AND DISCOVER. LOOK UP SALMON MIGRATIONS IN AN ENCYCLOPEDIA. WRITE A REPORT ABOUT THE SALMON'S TRAVELS. FIND OUT WHY IT RETURNS TO THE RIVER OF ITS BIRTH.

CHAPTER 12

Exploring Ocean Communities

PROBLEM:
What are the different zones of marine life?

12-1 LIVING THINGS ARE LIMITED

All living things are limited to certain kinds of environments. This is their home, or *HABITAT* (HAB-uh-tat).

Marine animals and plants are confined to certain environments. For example, some forms of fish are found only in very deep water. Others can be found only in shallow bays. Factors of the environment that determine how and where an organism lives are called *LIMITING FACTORS*. To meet its everyday needs, the organism must develop *ADAPTATIONS* (ad-ap-TAY-shuns), or changes in structure or function. If the organism can adapt, it survives. Otherwise, it dies.

What are the limiting factors in a habitat? How do they control and influence life?

12-2 PHYSICAL AND CHEMICAL ENVIRONMENT

All plants and animals of our land and water live together. They live in a narrow *sphere* called the *BIOSPHERE* (BY-uh-sfeer). The biosphere is made up of living things and their non-living environment. We call this the ecological system or *ECOSYSTEM*.

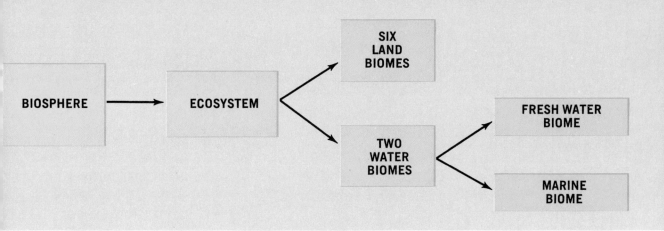

FIG. 99–1. An ecosystem is controlled by its living and nonliving factors.

A large area ecosystem is called a *BIOME* (BY-ome). Ecologists have divided the world into six land biomes (terrestrial; *terre* = "land") and two water biomes (aquatic; *aqua* = "water").

As you can guess, the two water biomes are the *freshwater biome* of rivers and lakes and the *marine biome* of oceans, bays, and seas.

12–3   WHERE DO THEY LIVE?

The first thing that we can ask about a living organism is: Where does it live? Is it found in sand or mud? High up on the beach or low in the water? The surface on which the marine organism lives is called the *SUBSTRATE* (SUB-strate). If we examine a rocky shore at low tide, we may find many animals hiding under the rocks. This hard substrate provides attachment and hiding places for many different creatures. These animals would have difficulty living on a sandy beach. Clearly, the sandy substrate would be a limiting factor.

Let us remember that the marine biome is both at the *edge* of the sea and *inside the waters* of the sea. The limiting factors would be different in each case.

Most marine life is found close to the shore, where conditions change rapidly from hour to hour as the tides rise and fall. Farther out on the continental shelf and in the shallower waters, conditions are again different. The presence of green plants provides large amounts of food.

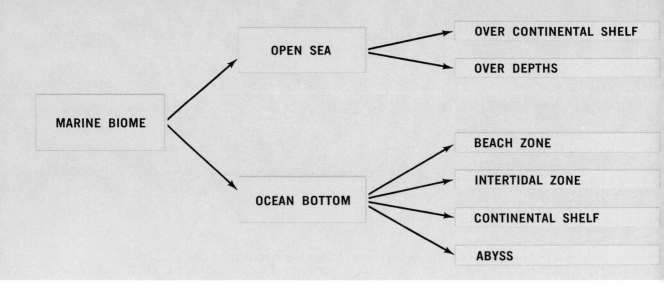

FIG. 100–1. The marine biome is made up of many different areas.

Out in the deep, cold ocean, the food supply drops sharply. The general marine population is small. There are two exceptions to this. Many fish are found in or near the currents. Below the ocean there are some regions called *banks*, which are high-level ground. Because the water is more shallow, these areas are the home of many fish. One example of this is the Grand Banks of Newfoundland, which are visited by many commercial fishermen.

12–4 ZONING IT OFF

Try walking along a sandy beach at low tide. Look for some evidence of life. Search under the sand or look into the water. The same type of walk along a rocky shore would be a lot easier, for you would find many examples of living things attached to the rocks (see Figure 102–3). Many of these organisms would probably be living in groups. We call such a group a *POPULATION*. This is what the ecologist calls an example of *ZONATION*—of organisms clustered in a particular zone. Why do we find populations living in one zone and not another?

When we study zonation, we must also look at the area under water. This means we must wait for low tide to uncover the ground below. This is the *INTERTIDAL* zone. Twice a day the bottom is covered and uncovered. The animals living here must adapt to periods of wetness and dryness.

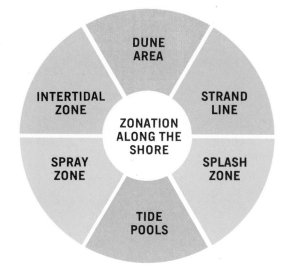

Fɪɢ. 101–1. Marine organisms can be found in many different zones of life.

LEARNED SO FAR

- All living things are confined to certain environments called *habitats*.
- Factors in the environment that determine how and where an organism lives are called *limiting factors*.
- Living things are found in *zones of life*.

12–5 ZONATION ALONG A SANDY BEACH

What kinds of zones shall we find along a sandy beach? Due to the shifting nature of the beach sands, zonation along a sandy beach cannot be seen so easily as it can in other areas. But if we look hard, we can still find some definite signs of life. What shall we find?

Beyond the high-tide mark, high up on the beach, we can find the *DUNE AREA*. What are the important limiting factors affecting life here? If you said wind and salt spray, you were correct.

The first group of dune plants facing the ocean must be able to adapt to salt spray and lack of fresh water. As a result, a very hardy type of beach grass is present. As we approach the side facing the land, grasses, shrubs, and trees take hold. Some of the trees look as if they have been twisted. This is caused by the salt spray.

Fig. 102–1.
The beach area at Andros Island in the Bahamas shows a strand line. What caused the formation of this zone?

Fig. 102–2.
Sand dunes at Point Lookout, New York. What limiting factors in the environment affect the life here?

Below the dune area, there is the *STRAND LINE*. It consists of dead seaweed, driftwood, and other articles washed up by the sea. High tides or unusually rough water can cause these materials to reach a high level. The strand line provides homes for many living things, such as insects, crabs, and worms.

The zones that lie between the tides are not too easy to find. If a certain animal is present in large numbers, we may call it a zone for this species. Clams and worms, for example, may be found in a moist-sand zone. To seek protection from the rough surf and to gain moisture when the tide is out, animals on sandy beaches must dig into the moist sand.

Fig. 102–3.
These periwinkles are found along a rocky beach.

12–6   WHAT ARE THE FEATURES OF A ROCKY BEACH?

Because of the hard surface of the rocks, animals in this zone cannot dig into the ground for protection. They must find a place to attach themselves. Otherwise, they would be carried away by the surf. They must also have special parts to attach themselves to the rocks. Starfish have sucking feet and mussels have tough threads to "glue" themselves to the rocks.

Because they cannot dig below the sands for moisture, these animals are left exposed to the air at low tide. How do you think they can survive the drying effects of the air?

Another feature of the rocky beach is the *TIDE POOLS*. They are found wherever spaces in the rocks trap pockets of water. These pools provide living places for small creatures at low tide. Typical organisms living in the pools are crabs, small fish, and algae. Animals living here at low tide must be able to withstand high temperatures and salinities. Can you think of reasons why?

FIG. 103–1.
What problems do these animals face living in the tide pools?

GO AND DISCOVER

INVESTIGATION: What are the characteristics of a tide pool?

PROCEDURES

1. Tide pools may be found on rocky coasts, salt marshes, or sandy beaches.
2. Investigate the factors of temperature and salinity using thermometers and pencil hydrometers (Chapter 10).
3. Fill two quart milk bottles with the water from the tide pool.
4. Measure the salinity and temperature of the water and compare them to those of the ocean and surrounding bays.
5. Record the types of animal and plant life found in the pool.

OBSERVATIONS AND ANALYSIS

1. What is the temperature of the tide pool? Is it higher or lower than that of the ocean water?
2. Where is the salinity higher?
3. What forms of life did you find inside the tide pool?

12–7 ZONATION ALONG A ROCKY BEACH

Rocky shores are the best places to look for zonation. When the surf hits the rocks, it creates droplets of water which bounce off to the higher areas. This forms a zone of life called the *SPLASH ZONE*. We can find blue-green algae and many snails living here.

FIG. 103–2.
Zonation along a rocky beach.

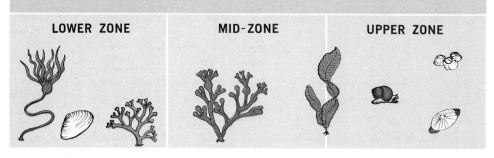

LOWER ZONE   **MID-ZONE**   **UPPER ZONE**

FIG. 104–1. Every zone has its animal and plant groups. Why can't the animals in the lower zone live in the upper zone?

12–8   MUD BEACHES AND SALT MARSHES

What zones of life do you think you can find along a mud beach?

The mud beach is found in calm and protected waters. The upper section of this community has a marsh area. Since the marsh environment is very important to the life of the sea, we shall give it special treatment in Chapter 19.

LEARNED SO FAR

● Animals living along a sandy beach dig into the sands for protection.
● To avoid being swept out to sea, organisms on rocky beaches attach themselves to the hard surfaces of the rocks.
● One feature of the rocky beach is the tide pool.
● Rocky shores are the best places to look for zonation.

Self-Study Guide for Chapter 12

I. KNOWING AND UNDERSTANDING. FIND THE ANSWER. WRITE IT IN YOUR NOTEBOOK.

1. When the tide is out, animals burrow into the wet sand to
   a. drink the water.
   b. escape the drying effects of the air.
   c. move closer to shore.
   d. hide under rocks.

2. Land plants living on sand dunes must be able to
   a. tolerate salt spray and lack of fresh water.
   b. lose water.
   c. live in fresh water.
   d. reproduce in quantity.
3. Animals that live on rocks find protection from the rough surf by
   a. moving onto the land.
   b. attaching to the rocks.
   c. swimming in the waves.
   d. burrowing.
4. One problem of organisms living in the tide pools is
   a. the heavy surf.
   b. in swimming.
   c. the high salinity.
   d. in breathing.

II. EXPLANATION, PLEASE.

1. Factors in the environment that determine how and where an organism lives are called limiting factors.
2. How is a biome different from an ecosystem?
3. What are the two most important environmental factors affecting plants on the sand dune?
4. How is a strand line formed on a sandy beach?

III. MATCH THE WORDS IN COLUMN *A* WITH THOSE IN COLUMN *B* IN YOUR NOTEBOOK.

A	*B*
1. Intertidal	a. Worm burrows in wet sand
2. Adapt	b. Shifting sands
3. Strand line	c. The science of ecology
4. Dune	d. Exposed to water and air
5. Zonation	e. Groups of organisms living together
	f. Materials brought in by waves

IV. TRUE OR FALSE? EXPLAIN YOUR ANSWERS.

1. Life on a rocky beach is different from that on a sandy beach.
2. Animals living along a rocky shore must be able to burrow.
3. A strand line is a good place to search for living things.
4. Animals living in tide pools must withstand high salinities.
5. A population consists of only one type of organism.

CHAPTER 13

Drifters of the Sea

PROBLEM:
*What is the importance
of microscopic life
in the sea?*

13–1 TEEMING WITH LIFE

The sea is the home of billions of living things—small and large, from jet black to white to brilliant red, from microscopic bacteria to 100-foot-long blue whales of 100 tons. There are the independent *producers* that make their own food. There are the quiet *consumers* and the savage killers.

All show adaptations to their biome and all are engaged in a struggle for existence.

How shall we begin to *classify* or arrange all living things? The chief grouping is into plants and animals.

Another very useful grouping is by methods of movement. Examine the chart below. This kind of grouping also tells us something about the food-getting problems and the behavior of each group.

FIG. 106–1.

LIFE IN THE SEA
ACCORDING TO LOCOMOTION

PLANKTON (PLANK-tun)	NEKTON (NEK-tun)	BENTHOS (BEN-thus)
Drifting Floating	Active swimming	Creeping Crawling Digging Attached

13-2 GREEN WATER AHEAD!

A cry of "Green water ahead!" echoes from a deep-sea fishing boat. What does this mean? Why should fishermen be interested in the color of the water? Simple! When the water is green, fishing may be good. Blue water indicates poor fishing. The green color is caused by the presence of millions of microscopic green plants, one kind of plankton. The word comes from a Greek word meaning "that which wanders or drifts." The plants are the food of many smaller animals. This attracts the fish that feed on these animals. Blue water contains very little microscopic life and is sometimes called "the desert of the sea."

What are these drifters like? Let us see.

13-3 A PLANKTON ROUNDUP

Imagine you are a marine biologist working on a special research vessel. You and your fellow scientists are preparing to lower a special cone-shaped net into the water. It will be towed behind the boat for 15 minutes. The holes in the net are so fine that any plankton will be drawn into the special collecting bottle.

What did we collect in our roundup? A microscope reveals a new world. Green plant cells with jewel-like coverings, animal-like creatures darting back and forth.

FIG. 107–1. These scientists are using a plankton net. What kinds of life will the net pick up? What kinds will it not? Explain.

Fig. 108–1.

13–4 GRASSES OF THE SEAS

The microscopic green plants are important to all life in the sea. Strange as it may seem, these tiny plants supply food for millions of other creatures. They are called the *PHYTO-PLANKTON* (fy-to-PLANK-tun) (*phyto* = "plant"). In their short life span, these green cells capture the sun's energy for food-making. Sunlight is absorbed by *CHLOROPHYLL* (KLO-ruh-fil), a chemical in their cells. The sun's energy is used to combine molecules of carbon dioxide and water to produce sugar for energy and growth. We call this process *PHOTOSYNTHE-SIS* (fo-tuh-SIN-thuh-sis). The plant releases oxygen and water as by-products. It has been estimated that 80 to 90 percent of the world's oxygen is released by the phytoplankton! Just think, a molecule of oxygen that you are now breathing may have been released by a plankton cell. Again, we are talking of the carbon-dioxide–oxygen cycle. Examine it in Figure 108–2.

Fig. 108–2. What substances are used by the cell? What is made? What is released?

Raw materials	Light energy	Useful food	+	Waste gas
Water + Carbon dioxide	Chemical change caused by the sun $\longrightarrow$	Simple sugar		Oxygen + Water
$12H_2O + 6CO_2$	$\longrightarrow$	$C_6H_{12}O_6 + 6O_2 + 6H_2O$		

13–5 SNOWFLAKES OF THE SEA

Have you ever looked at snowflakes very closely? They are formed in beautiful, complex shapes. Next time it snows, examine the flakes with a magnifying glass. You may think of snowflakes if you look at a type of plant plankton called a *DIATOM* (DY-uh-tum). In any given sample of seawater collected, you will find great numbers of these cells. When we examine them through a microscope, diatoms are yellow-green or "golden" in color. Each cell has a "glass" outer wall, as shown in Figure 109–1. It is made up of two halves that fit into one another.

108

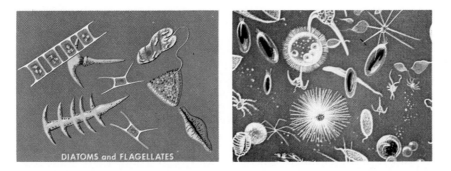

Fig. 109–1. Various types of plankton. How are they different? How are they similar?

When diatoms die, their shells sink to the bottom of the sea. Layers and layers of these shells have been built up, leaving great deposits. We call the sediments *DIATOMACEOUS EARTH* (dy-uh-tuh-MAY-shus). Diatomaceous earth is a useful product which we shall talk about in a later chapter.

13–6 A LIGHT SHOW BY THE SEA

Walk down to the sea on a dark summer's night. Throw a stone into the water. You may see flashes of light. This is called *BIOLUMINESCENCE* (by-o-loo-muh-NES-uns). It is light without heat and is sometimes called "cold light." This light is produced by tiny plants called *DINOFLAGELLATES* (dy-no-FLAJ-uh-lates). They are considered part of the phytoplankton group. But many scientists feel that these are neither true plants nor animals. Many have chlorophyll, which is either brown or green. They can make their own food. Others swim around and capture their own food. Where would you place them on the scale of life?

13–7 ALL KINDS OF PHYTOPLANKTON

Phytoplankton that are green belong to the plant group called *ALGAE* (AL-jee). But not all phytoplankton are green; not all contain chlorophyll. The ocean is the home of countless billions of cells without chlorophyll. This group is called *FUNGI* (FUN-jy). Ocean bacteria are fungi. They are extremely important in the ocean cycles, since they decay dead plants and animals. In this way, elements are returned to the sea for reuse.

- Life in the sea is often grouped according to type of locomotion.
- Microscopic organisms that float in the currents are called plankton.
- Plankton include both plant and animal forms.
- Phytoplankton use sunlight to make their own food by photosynthesis.

13–8 GRAZERS OF THE SEA

A farmer sends his cattle to pasture to feed on the rich grasses. The cattle are called grazing animals. In the sea, we also find grazers. These are the animal plankton, or *ZOOPLANKTON* (zo-uh-PLANK-tun). Their diets consist of the microscopic plants.

What can we find if we search through a zooplankton sample? Common "citizens" are shrimplike creatures called *COPE-PODS* (KO-puh-podz), which dart back and forth. Immature or *LARVAL* (LAR-vul) forms of crabs, jellyfish, barnacles, and fish move slowly. Under high power magnification, we see tiny one-celled animals, the *PROTOZOA* (pro-tuh-ZO-uh). A common type has a jewel-like shell. These are the *FORAMIN-IFERA* (forams, for short). Inside this shell is a one-celled animal which builds this beautiful design. When forams die, the shells settle to the bottom of the ocean. The great white cliffs of Dover, England, are made of the remains of these shells.

13–9 YOUR OWN PLANKTON NET

Fig. 110–1. Zooplankton are animals that feed on the plants. How do they differ from plants?

INVESTIGATION: How can we collect plankton from local waters?

PROCEDURES
1. Construct the simple plankton net as shown in the diagram.

2. Place your net in the water, making sure it is drifting in the current.
3. Allow the net to remain in the water for 15 minutes.
4. Haul in the net and remove the collecting bottle.
5. Transfer one or two drops of the water from the bottle to a slide. Add a cover slip and observe under the microscope. (Ask your teacher for help in identification.)
6. Try collecting samples from a bay, a marsh, and a river.
7. If salt water is not available, try collecting from fresh water.

OBSERVATIONS AND ANALYSIS
1. What types of plankton were found in the greatest numbers? Why?
2. Using pictures in reference texts, see if you can identify the types in your sample. Draw a few simple types.

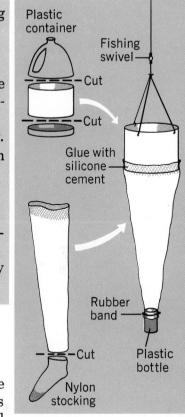

FIG. 111–1.

13–10 FOOD CHAINS

We learned in Chapter 11 that all plants and animals in the ecosystem need energy to live. Green plants are the producers from which all the organisms get the energy they need. All these organisms in a community are joined together for their food needs—almost like the links that form a chain. The way in which these needs of ocean life are related is shown by the diagram below.

Diatoms Protozoa	Eaten → By	Small Crustacean and Copepods	Eaten → By	Small Fish	Eaten → By	Striped Bass

We call this example a *food chain*. Why do the fish at the end of the chain depend upon the plants at the beginning of the chain?

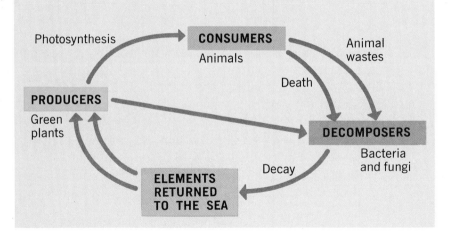

Fɪɢ. 112–1. Which are the producers? Consumers? How does this differ from the food chain?

13–11 FOOD WEBS

What do you think of when you hear the word *web?* Probably a network, such as a spider's web. The relationship of the food chain is really not so simple as it looks. Rather, it is like a web. Usually, food chains branch out to form food webs. For example, the small fish may eat other organisms. There may be many different animals and plants involved, each depending upon one another.

13–12 THE CENTRAL IDEA OF NUTRITION

Sea organisms are either producers, consumers, or decomposers. The green algae make their own food. Animals eat the food. The bacteria are decomposers. They break down dead organic material to form the elements needed in recycling living things.

As you can see, nutrition is a basic relationship in the sea. Perhaps this little poem sums it up:

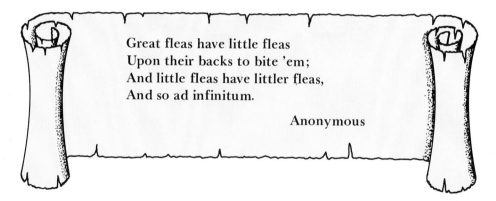

Great fleas have little fleas
Upon their backs to bite 'em;
And little fleas have littler fleas,
And so ad infinitum.

Anonymous

● Animals in the sea depend, directly or indirectly, upon plankton for food.
● The food cycle in the sea may form a food chain.
● When food chains cross and crisscross, they form a food web.

Self-Study Guide for Chapter 13

I. KNOWING AND UNDERSTANDING. FIND THE ANSWER. WRITE IT IN YOUR NOTEBOOK.

1. The microscopic green plants of the sea are important because they
   a. secrete shells.
   b. drift with the currents.
   c. provide food for the zooplankton.
   d. give color to the water.
2. An example of a food chain would be
   a. zooplankton-tuna-herring-phytoplankton.
   b. tuna-zooplankton-phytoplankton-herring.
   c. phytoplankton-zooplankton-herring-tuna.
   d. herring-tuna-zooplankton-tuna.
3. All the following would be classified under the heading plankton except
   a. diatoms.
   b. fish.
   c. copepods.
   d. protozoa.
4. The animals at the end of a food chain depend upon
   a. the phytoplankton directly.
   b. the zooplankton directly.
   c. the animal group directly below them in the chain.
   d. none of the above choices.

II. READ ALL ABOUT IT.

1. Read about bioluminescence in an encyclopedia.
2. Find out why light is produced.
3. What other organisms produce light?

III. FIND THE EXPLANATION. IN WHICH SECTION OF THE CHAP-
TER IS THE ANSWER TO EACH OF THE FOLLOWING QUES-
TIONS? WRITE THE QUESTION AND THE ANSWER IN YOUR
NOTEBOOK.

1. Why do the phytoplankton form the basis of life in the sea?
2. What are diatoms?
3. What organisms are involved in the process of decay?
4. What do we mean by a food web?

IV. MATCH THE WORDS IN COLUMN *A* WITH THOSE IN COLUMN
B IN YOUR NOTEBOOK.

A	*B*
1. Bioluminescence	a. Using light to make food
2. Foraminifera	b. One organism dependent on next for energy
3. Copepods	c. One-celled green plant
4. Chlorophyll	d. Green chemical needed to absorb light
5. Photosynthesis	e. Zooplankton organism
6. Food chain	f . Larva
7. Diatoms	g. Chalk cliffs
	h. Process which absorbs oxygen
	i . Jellyfish
	j . Ability to produce light

V. TRUE OR FALSE? IF THE STATEMENT IS TRUE, WRITE TRUE
IN YOUR NOTEBOOK. IF THE STATEMENT IS FALSE, CHANGE
THE UNDERLINED WORD TO MAKE THE STATEMENT TRUE.

1. Diatomaceous earth is formed from skeletal remains of diatoms.
2. Man could be placed at the beginning of a food web.
3. Zooplankton are the basis of life in the sea since they capture
the sun's energy.

VI. FOR THE JUNIOR SCIENTIST—TRY IT YOURSELF. USING YOUR
HOMEMADE PLANKTON NET, COLLECT WATER SAMPLES FROM
A BAY OR LAKE.

1. Collect water samples
   a. near the surface.
   b. near the middle.
   c. on the bottom.
2. Which sample had the largest amount of plankton?
3. Explain your answer to the above question.

VII. A FOOD PYRAMID IS ANOTHER EXAMPLE OF HOW THE CREA-
TURES OF THE SEA DEPEND ON ONE ANOTHER FOR FOOD.
STUDY THE DIAGRAM AND ANSWER THE QUESTIONS BELOW.
DO NOT WRITE IN THIS BOOK.

1. Where are the greatest numbers of living things?
2. Where are the producers? How do you know?
3. List examples of organisms that should go into each section of
the pyramid.

FIG. 115–1.

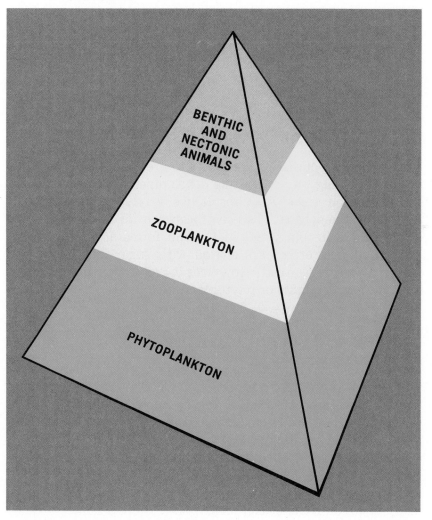

CHAPTER 14

Marine Plants

14–1 FOOD FOR THE FUTURE?

As the world's population continues to grow, land once used for farming is giving way to housing developments, factories, roads, and recreation areas. As a result, we may soon have to look for food in the oceans. The use of seaweed for food is not new. Many people in Japan eat it. Certain forms are cooked with meats and rice, others are coated with sugar and served for dessert. What is seaweed? How does it grow? How does it differ from the simple plants or phytoplankton?

14–2 SEAWEED AT THE SEASHORE

In our previous chapter, we studied microscopic plankton. If you go down to the seashore, you will see some very large plants. Some are attached to rocks; some are floating in the water. No, these are not "lost" land plants. They are at home in the sea. We usually call them *seaweeds*.

The algae we studied earlier were one-celled. Some form *colonies* of single cells. Examine a seaweed under the microscope. You will find that its *TISSUES* are made of many cells, many of which have special jobs.

FIG. 116–1.

116

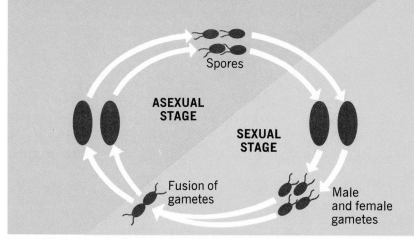

FIG. 117–1. Seaweeds reproduce by means of spores. Do you think this is an adaptation to life in water? Explain your answer.

Unlike land plants, seaweeds are simple plants also belonging to the algae group. They do not have true roots, true stems, or true leaves. Furthermore, they do not reproduce by flowers and seeds. In order to reproduce, some seaweeds send out tiny swimming structures called *SPORES* (SPORZ). These are single cells that can move on their own. The spore separates from the parent to produce a new plant. Thousands of spores from a single plant produce thousands of plants.

14–3 NICKNAMES OR SCIENTIFIC NAMES?

Plants and animals often have common names or nicknames. But their real names are scientific and systematic.

Every organism is given two scientific names. The first is the name of the *GENUS* (JEE-nus), or the large group. Following this is the *SPECIES* (SPEE-sheez) name. Thus, humans belong to the genus *Homo*, species *sapiens*. The house fly is *Musca domestica;* the tiger is *Felis tigris;* the cat is *Felis domestica.* Similar organisms are placed in the same grouping if they have the same structures.

Why use scientific naming? When biologists use these terms, they can understand each other even though they speak different languages. Think of the word *seaweed*. To most people it means a weed that lives in the sea. A weed is also a plant that springs up where it is not wanted and has roots, leaves, and flowers. But the land weed and seaweed are definitely not related! This is why we must be specific with our names.

FIG. 117–2. In Japan, seaweed is first dried in the sun and then used for food. What are some problems in using seaweed as food?

14–4 GROUPING BY COLORS

Seaweeds are algae. They have chlorophyll and can make their own food. However, seaweeds have several other pigments in addition to chlorophyll. Some of the pigments mask the green.

We classify the seaweeds according to the colors of their pigments.

LEARNED SO FAR

- Seaweeds are large marine plants consisting of many cells.
- Seaweeds are algae which come in several colors that sometimes mask the green.
- Seaweeds are plants with simple structure that reproduce by spores and sexual cells.
- Some seaweeds are now used as food.

14–5 THE GREENS

Green seaweeds grow close to the shore, just below the tide mark. Some grow in long sections called filaments (FIL-uh-ments). Some grow in branches. Some grow as large flat sheets resembling lettuce.

14–6 THE BROWNS

The recipe for a New England clambake calls for fish chowder, lobsters, clams, corn, potatoes, and onions. The lobsters and clams are first packed in foil and then wrapped in *rockweed* for cooking. What is rockweed? It is one of the brown seaweeds called *FUCUS* (FYOO-kus). Most seaweeds are in the brown group.

Rockweeds, like many of these plants, float on the surface because they have air-filled sacs called *BLADDERS* (BLAD-durz). They generally grow attached to rocks in shallow waters. When the tide moves out, they are exposed. Perhaps you have seen rockweed at your neighborhood seafood store. It is used to wrap fresh oysters and crabs to keep them from drying out.

Fig. 118–1.
Codium and *Ulva*. How are these two plants adapted to their environment?

The most famous of the brown seaweeds is *Sargassum*. This seaweed floats in huge patches in an area of the Atlantic known as the Sargasso Sea (Chapter 7). Christopher Columbus is said to have run into it on his first Atlantic crossing. The men on board ship were afraid they had run aground, since seaweed is usually found near the shore. To the biologist, this seaweed area is known as a "desert of the sea," since fish life is not very plentiful. Because plankton are not present, other creatures are not attracted to the area.

There is a seaweed whose mass is as great as that of a large tree and which can grow to be between 200 and 300 feet tall. This is kelp, the earth's fastest-growing plant. Much kelp is found in the cool waters of the Pacific off the western shores of the United States.

14–7 THE REDS

Red seaweeds are best known for their beauty and form. Since the red pigment absorbs more blue and violet light, it is found in cooler and deeper water. Red seaweeds contain green chlorophyll; a red pigment masks the green.

Fig. 119–1. Kelp is harvested off the California coast. Machinery hauls the cut seaweed aboard. How is it useful to man?

GO AND DISCOVER

INVESTIGATION: What types of seaweeds can be found along the shore?

PROCEDURES
A. Collection
   1. Investigate a beach at low tide. Try to find examples of green, brown, and red seaweeds.
   2. Place them in a bucket with seawater; keep them as cool as possible.
B. Mounting and Identification
   1. Float seaweed in a pan of seawater.
   2. Slide a 5 × 8 inch card below the plant.
   3. Float seaweed into position, raise card, and remove it.
   4. Cover with several layers of newspaper for drying. (A brick or several heavy books placed on top will help proper and flat drying.)

5. Leave the setup for two days.
6. When dry, cover the plants with a clear plastic wrap.

OBSERVATIONS AND ANALYSIS
1. What seaweeds were more common?
2. Describe differences in greens, browns, and reds.

14–8 SEAWEEDS, ECOLOGY, AND PEOPLE

Seaweeds play a great role in the survival of animal life. They add to the oxygen supply of the sea and in turn remove carbon dioxide from the water. Seaweeds also supply animals with sources of food and protection. Blending in with the colors, many animals find good hiding places where they can also find moisture. This prevents them from drying out when the tide moves out.

Are seaweeds useful to man? Most definitely! We have already mentioned the use of seaweeds as food in Japan. The chart below shows some other uses.

USEFUL SEAWEEDS

Seaweed	Type	Product
Kelp	Brown	Iodine extracted; fertilizer, dried and spread like manure; Algin— used in syrups, puddings, salad dressings, and ice cream
Chondrus	Red	Vegetable and fillers for soup; ice cream; hand lotion
Gelidium	Red	Agar for growing bacteria in labs

LEARNED SO FAR

- Seaweeds can be classified into the greens, browns, and reds.
- Seaweeds show many adaptations to their environment.
- Seaweeds supply animals with shelter, food, and oxygen.
- Some seaweeds are processed for commercial use.

Self-Study Guide for Chapter 14

I. KNOWING AND UNDERSTANDING. FIND THE ANSWER. WRITE IT IN YOUR NOTEBOOK.

1. Seaweeds are known as simple plants because
   a. they lack chlorophyll.
   b. they lack roots, stems, and leaves.
   c. some are brown.
   d. some produce seeds.
2. Seaweeds can reproduce by
   a. sending out spores.
   b. producing runners.
   c. moving around.
   d. growing roots.
3. Seaweeds can manufacture their own food because
   a. they absorb what they need.
   b. they can capture the sun's energy.
   c. they can find their own food.
   d. they can borrow from other plants.
4. Red seaweeds are found at greater depths because
   a. they can take the pressure.
   b. they need more CO_2.
   c. they absorb more blue and violet light.
   d. it's cooler at this depth.

II. FIND THE EXPLANATION. IN WHICH SECTION OF THE CHAPTER IS THE ANSWER TO EACH OF THE FOLLOWING QUESTIONS? WRITE THE QUESTION AND THE ANSWER IN YOUR NOTEBOOK.

1. Why are the seaweeds grouped with the algae?
2. Why do biologists use scientific names?
3. How are the rockweeds able to stay afloat?
4. Why are seaweeds important to animal life?

III. TRUE OR FALSE? EXPLAIN YOUR ANSWERS.

1. Brown seaweeds do not have chlorophyll.
2. Red seaweeds are found at greater depths.
3. Seaweeds are plants that have roots, stems, and leaves.
4. Scientific grouping involves grouping organisms with the same characteristics.

IV. MATCH THE WORDS IN COLUMN *A* WITH THE WORDS IN COLUMN *B* IN YOUR NOTEBOOK.

A	*B*
1. Spores	a. Floating brown seaweed
2. Genus	b. Helps seaweed float
3. Filaments	c. Seaweed reproduction
4. Bladders	d. Chemical extract from seaweed
5. Algin	e. Green seaweed
6. *Sargassum*	f. Long strand of seaweed
7. *Ulva*—sea lettuce	g. Scientific naming
	h. Produces seeds
	i. Has roots, stems, leaves

V. ON THE LADDER OF UNDERSTANDING. WRITE THE SENTENCES IN YOUR NOTEBOOK. FILL IN THE CORRECT WORD.

1. Food-making in plants is called —————.
2. Minute organisms, both plant and animal, make up the ————— layer of the sea.
3. In plants, sunlight is absorbed by the —————.
4. In the food-making process, green plants give off the gas —————.
5. The seaweeds belong to the group of plants called —————.

VI. MAKE A CHART OF THE MAJOR TYPES OF SEAWEEDS. INCLUDE ONE EXAMPLE OF EACH.

VII. USING THE TECHNIQUE OUTLINED ON PAGE 119, MAKE A COLLECTION OF MANY DIFFERENT TYPES OF SEAWEEDS. PLACE THEM IN AN ALBUM FOR FUTURE REFERENCE. USE THE FOLLOWING FORM TO LABEL YOUR COLLECTION. DO NOT WRITE ON THE SAMPLE BELOW.

> ## SEAWEED IDENTIFICATION INFORMATION
>
> Type ——————————————————
> Where found ——————————————
> Date ——————————————————
> Environment: In bright sunlight at base of rocks on the south side of the bay. Temp. 20.5°C at 3:00 P.M. (Example only.)
> *Collected by:* ————————————

CHAPTER 15

*Marine
Animals*

PROBLEM:
*What are some sea
animals without
backbones?*

15-1 WITH BACKBONE...WITHOUT BACKBONE

Have you ever heard someone say, "He's like a jellyfish; he's spineless." The person is being compared to a jellyfish; when taken out of the water, the animal collapses.

Zoologists classify animals into nine major groups called *PHYLA* (FY-luh) (singular: phylum). Animals in eight of the phyla do not have spines or backbones. Animals in the ninth phylum do have a backbone or spine (see Section 17-1). Those with backbones are called *CHORDATES* (KOR-dates). These include a more developed group called *VERTEBRATES* (VUR-tuh-brates). The other eight phyla together are sometimes called IN*VERTEBRATES* (*in* = "not, without").

ANIMAL KINGDOM { 8 PHYLA: Invertebrates
1 PHYLUM: Chordates
(include vertebrates)

15-2 A SURVEY OF INVERTEBRATES

Most animals, on both land and sea, are invertebrates. Marine invertebrates lack internal support for their bodies; they collapse easily when removed from the water. Only lobsters, crabs, and others with an outside skeleton or shell keep their shape outside the water. Other members of the invertebrates include shrimps, worms, starfish, and sponges.

We are going to survey some of the major invertebrate phyla, progressing from the simplest to the most advanced. Before you read ahead, examine the "Tree of Life," page 156. As you can guess, animals on the lowest branches are not as complex as those on the highest. How are these animals related to one another?

15-3 ANIMALS WITH PORES

Imagine a piece of beef liver shaped a little like a basketball with holes in it. This will give you an idea of the body design of a typical sponge. Most sponges grow attached and often look like plants. Some are so tiny they live in snail shells. Others grow to 2 or 3 feet. They are found in many colors.

The sponges are simple in structure; they have bodies made up of many cells in two layers. Sponges take in water through their pores to strain out the microscopic animals and plants. Some of the sponge's cells create currents of water; others grasp food from the incoming water and digest it.

The sponge body is supported by a skeleton made up of hundreds of tiny structures called *SPICULES* (SPIK-yoolz). Spicules are made of either lime or a glasslike substance called

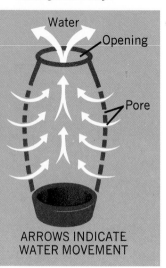

FIG. 124–1. The sponge body has many holes or pores. How does water move through its body?

Water

Opening

Pore

ARROWS INDICATE WATER MOVEMENT

FIG. 124–2. On Florida's Gulf Coast, fishermen collect sponges for commercial use. How do the spicules help the animal in its struggle for existence?

CRETE

SILICA (SIL-uh-kuh). When the sponge dies, the spicules are left behind to form beautiful and interesting designs. A few kinds of sponges build their skeletons out of a material called *SPONGIN* (SPUN-jun). These are the sponges that we use in our homes. They are collected by divers on Florida's Gulf Coast. Most sponges are marine. A few are freshwater.

Fig. 125–1.
Red-beard sponges may be found growing in shallow waters along the Atlantic Coast. How do they fit into the food pyramid?

Fig. 125–2.
Portuguese men-of-war float in the currents of the ocean. They capture fish with their tentacles. How do they fit into the food pyramid?

15–4 ANIMALS WITH STINGING CELLS

A skin diver exploring tropical waters noticed a large bag-shaped object on the surface. Moments later he felt a sharp pain in his leg; red, "angry" welts appeared over his skin. The diver had become entangled in the *TENTACLES* (TEN-tuh-kulz) of a large *PORTUGUESE MAN-OF-WAR*. Inside the tentacles thousands of stinging cells discharged their poisons into the diver's skin. The man-of-war is not one animal but thousands of tiny animals that live in the tentacles. The bag is the result of a gas released by the animals.

Fig. 125–3.
Sea Anemone.

Most of us, fortunately, do not have encounters with Portuguese men-of-war. But many of us have experienced the sting of the more common jellyfish. This phylum is known as the cup-shaped phylum. It consists of two layers of cells, with a jelly-like material between the layers. All have stinging cells filled with a powerful poison. Members of the group include the *jelly-fish, sea anemone* (uh-NEM-uh-nee), and *corals*.

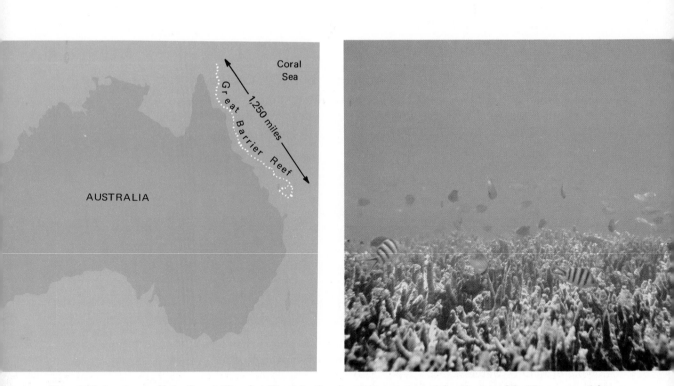

FIG. 126–1. Australia's Great Barrier Reef is the largest coral reef in the world. How was this reef formed?

15–5 CORALS AND CORAL REEFS

FIG. 126–2. The shallow, quiet waters on the land side of the reef form the home for a great variety of marine life.

Distant places with strange-sounding names! Bikini Atoll, Christmas Island, Canton, Eniwetok, the Great Barrier Reef, Cozumel. . . . Where are they? What are they? Are they the homes of castaway sailors like Robinson Crusoe? These are all coral formations.

Coral reefs are found in three basic forms. A *FRINGING REEF* develops close to shore, with a shallow channel between the reef and shore. The coral is built outward toward the sun and the open sea. A *BARRIER REEF* is usually far from land. The channel between the reef and shore is deep enough for ships to pass through. The Great Barrier Reef in Australia (Figure 126–1) is almost 1,250 miles long and is separated from the land by a 10-mile passage. *ATOLLS* (see Section 6–7) are reefs that are horseshoe-shaped and form little islands. In the center of the atoll is a *LAGOON* (luh-GOON), or small bay.

126

- Marine animals without backbones are called invertebrates. Animals are classed together in a phylum when they resemble one another closely.
- Members of the sponge group all have pores.
- Animals of the cup-shaped phylum all have stinging cells.

15–6 ALL KINDS OF WORMS

All *worms*, to an untrained eye, seem to be alike—but they are not. There are *roundworms*, *flatworms*, and *segmented* (sectioned) worms. Members of all three groups are found in the sea.

Marine worms swim free, creep, crawl, and burrow under rocks or sand. Some are vegetarian; others eat smaller worms.

When you visit the shore at low tide, turn over some rocks and see if you can find some worms. You may come across a large worm that looks as if it were divided into compartments. Closer inspection may reveal a short head with two claws. This is the clam worm, or *NEREIS* (NEE-ree-us). Members of this group all have bodies that are divided into sections resembling rings. A well-known example is the common earthworm. Others are the feather worms and fan worms. Worms are the food of many larger and more powerful marine animals.

15–7 SPINY-SKINNED ANIMALS

Two spiny-skinned animals that you will see quite often are the *starfish* and the *sea urchin*. All over the body of the starfish there are raised plates of lime. The sea urchin has actual spines that stick out of its fused skeleton of lime. These spines can give you a nasty cut.

The starfish has five arms spreading outward from a central disk. Underneath each arm are rows of suckers used for attachment. On the top surface of the animal is a small pore through which water enters. The water moves to specialized tubes, then into the suckers, or "tube feet." This water system helps create the suction for attachment. Alternate suction and release allow the starfish to "walk" ever so slowly.

FIG. 127–1. Starfish and sea urchin are both members of the group of spiny-skinned animals. How are they different?

127

FIG. 128–1. This starfish has made a start in regrowing its lost arms. Does chopping up starfish and throwing them back into the water stop damage to oyster crops? Explain.

The starfish is one of the worst enemies of the oyster. Using its great powers of suction, it attacks by wrapping itself around the oyster's shell. This forces the shell to open a little bit. It then passes its saclike stomach into the oyster, where it digests the oyster's flesh.

LEARNED SO FAR

● Marine worms may belong to the flatworm, roundworm, or segmented-worm group.
● Featherworms and clam worms are segmented.
● Starfish, sea urchins, and sea cucumbers belong to the spiny-skinned group.

Self-Study Guide for Chapter 15

I. KNOWING AND UNDERSTANDING. FIND THE ANSWER. WRITE IT IN YOUR NOTEBOOK.

    1. Jellyfish collapse when they are removed from the water because
       a. they lack backbones.
       b. air pushes on them.
       c. they have outside skeletons.
       d. of the sunlight.
    2. Lobsters and crabs do not collapse when removed from the water because
       a. they are stronger.
       b. they have outside support.
       c. they have backbones.
       d. they live on land.

3. In order to feed, a sponge
    a. must take in water through its pores.
    b. must move around and capture its food.
    c. must swim.
    d. must sting its food.
4. Animals are placed in a phylum because
    a. they differ from one another.
    b. they resemble one another closely in structure.
    c. they live in the same place.
    d. they eat the same foods.

II. EXPLANATION, PLEASE. IN WHICH SECTION OF THE CHAPTER IS THE ANSWER TO EACH OF THE FOLLOWING QUESTIONS? WRITE THE QUESTION AND THE ANSWER IN YOUR NOTEBOOK.

1. In what way is the barrier reef different from a fringing reef?
2. How is a stinging-celled animal different from a sponge?

III. FIND THE OUTSIDER. WHICH WORD DOES NOT BELONG WITH THE OTHERS?

1. Red-beard sponge, sulfur sponge, jellyfish, bath sponge.
2. Jellyfish, Portuguese man-of-war, coral animals, starfish.
3. Fringing reef, barrier reef, atoll, lagoon.
4. Feather worm, nereis, clam worm, sea anemone.
5. Starfish, sea urchin, sea anemone.

IV. PUT ON YOUR THINKING CAP.

1. How are chordates like vertebrates? How are they different?
2. Can you make bath sponges from sponges that have spicules? Explain.
3. Can sea anemones move away from enemies? Why not? How do they protect themselves?

CHAPTER 16   *More Marine Animals without Backbones*

PROBLEM:
What are some other marine invertebrates?

16–1 ANIMALS WITH JOINTED LEGS

Think of animals with hard *outer* skeletons whose jointed legs can bend. This is the jointed-leg phylum. Their bodies are in *sections*. The legs and sections are moved by muscles. Members of this group can creep, crawl, or hop. Some of them can swim, but only slightly.

Do these animals remind you of any land animals you know? You are right! The insects and spiders are their "cousins" on land. This is the phylum called *ARTHROPOD*S (AR-thruh-podz). Most marine arthropods belong to a subgroup called *CRUSTACEANS* (krus-TAY-shunz). These include barnacles, lobsters, shrimps, and crabs.

16–2 THE AMERICAN LOBSTER

So often when we think of a fine seafood dinner, we think of lobster. No other marine animal is prized so highly for its meat. One of the great lobster fishing areas is just off the coast of Maine. Fishermen set special baited traps; when the lobster enters, the trap closes.

FIG. 131–1. Fishermen trap lobsters off the Maine coast. The wooden traps are lowered and attached to floats.

The lobster has five pairs of legs (ten legs in all) attached to its chest region. Anyone who has foolishly put his fingers near the first pair never forgets them. These are the *PINCERS* (pinchers), which grab other animals for the lobster's dinner.

Lobsters use *GILLS* to remove oxygen from the water. They have well-developed eyes and feelers, or *ANTENNAE* (an-TEN-ee), for receiving sensations from the environment.

The female lobster lays between 8,000 and 10,000 eggs. As they leave her body, they are fertilized by the male. The eggs stick to special structures on the female. Young lobsters hatch from eggs into a larval stage. They quickly undergo many changes before they reach the adult stage.

FIG. 131–3. Eggs remain attached to the female lobster. What happens to the young lobster after hatching?

FIG. 131–2. Diagram of major parts of the common lobster. Can you give the function of each part?

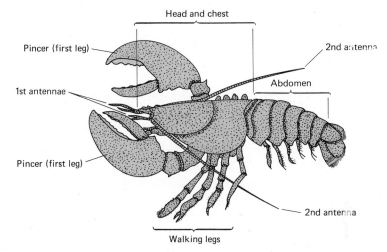

Head and chest

Pincer (first leg)

2nd antenna

1st antennae

Abdomen

Pincer (first leg)

2nd antenna

Walking legs

Fig. 132–1.
Hermit crabs live in the empty shells of snails. How are they related to the lobster?

Fig. 132–2.
Barnacles do not seem to resemble crustaceans. What problems do they cause for man?

16–3 CLOWNS OF THE SEA

Some very amusing creatures of the sea are the crabs. One fellow that is most easily observed is the ever-present *HERMIT CRAB*. This small crustacean seeks out the empty shells of snails. Running across the sea bottom, hermit crabs look very amusing as they carry their homes on their backs. As the hermit crab grows, it has to keep looking for larger shells.

16–4 THE UNUSUAL CRUSTACEAN

Ask a boat owner what marine animal is most annoying. He will probably tell you it is the *BARNACLE* (BAR-nuh-kul). These crustaceans attach themselves to boat bottoms and can slow them down. How do you think they do this? Boat owners have to scrape their boats each year.

At first glance, the barnacle does not resemble any other crustacean. Most often you will find barnacles firmly attached to rocks, boats, and pier pilings. In spite of their strange appearance, scientists recognize them as crustaceans.

The young barnacle is a true swimming form. As it grows older, it fixes itself to a rock and secretes a shell around itself. The barnacle feeds by extending feather-like feet through the opening of its shell. One scientist has described a barnacle as an animal that lies on its back and kicks its food into its mouth with its feet.

Barnacles produce a very strong cement that helps them to stick to rocks even though there are powerful waves. For this reason, dentists are testing barnacle cement for possible use as a filling for teeth.

16–5 THE LIVING FOSSIL

FOSSILS (FOS-ulz) are the remains of animals that roamed the earth many millions of years ago and were preserved when they died. Scientists call the *HORSESHOE CRAB* a "living fossil" because the crabs living today closely resemble the fossil remains of crabs that lived millions of years ago. In fact, these crabs do not belong to the crustacean family but are more closely related to the spiders.

● Animals with jointed legs and outside skeletons belong to the arthropod phylum.
● Most marine arthropods belong to the subgroup Crustacea. Crustaceans include lobsters, crabs, and barnacles.
● The horseshoe crab is related to the spider family on land.

16–6   THE SHELLED-ANIMAL PHYLUM

The second largest group of invertebrates belongs to the phylum called *MOLLUSKS* (MOL-usks), more commonly known as shellfish. They are also called the soft-bodied animals because the entire mass of the animal is very soft. All mollusks have some shell formation and a special fold of skin called the *MANTLE* (MAN-tul). Marine animals included in this group are the snails, clams, oysters, mussels, octopuses, and squid.

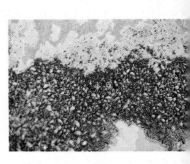

FIG. 133–1. Mussels.

Some mollusks have one shell, others two. The octopus and squid have only the tiny remains of a shell.

Do mollusks have locomotion? Well, the snail may be slow, but he sure does move. Clams and oysters crawl in the mud by sticking out a single muscular "foot" from the shell. As the muscle expands and contracts, the animal is pulled along.

16–7   THE CLAM

The clam has certain features in common with such animals as the oyster, scallop, and mussel. All these mollusks have *double* shells which are opened and closed by the action of very powerful muscles. The body of the animal fits between the two halves of the shell. Follow the arrows in the figure below to get an idea of how the clam breathes and feeds.

FIG. 133–2.
The clam moves by means of a single "foot."

FIG. 133–3. Follow the movement of food in the clam.

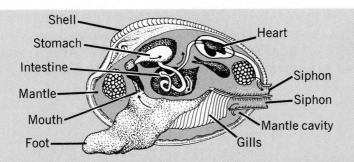

Shell — Heart — Stomach — Intestine — Siphon — Mantle — Siphon — Mouth — Mantle cavity — Foot — Gills

133

FIG. 134–1. Pearl culturing in Japan.

16–8 OYSTERS: FOOD OR PEARLS?

Oysters are double-shelled mollusks that live best in quiet bays of low salinity. Their meat is tasty and very nutritious. People used to eat oysters only during the cooler months of the year, September through April. Because of modern refrigeration, oysters can now be eaten throughout the year.

Oysters grow attached to the sea bottom. A single oyster can produce 100 million eggs at one time.

In Japan, native women divers descend into the depths in search of special pearl oysters. It has been said that these divers can stay under water for two or three minutes without using any equipment. How is this possible?

In order to form these valuable pearls, a grain of sand must get under the shell. This object is covered by a substance called mother-of-pearl. This sometimes occurs in nature. The famous cultured pearls of the Orient are raised artificially. Young oysters are chosen. A slit is made in the mantle and a tiny bit of shell is inserted. The oyster is then returned to the water to grow on wooden floats in oyster "beds." After a time, the oyster is opened and a beautiful pearl is found to have developed inside.

What terrible stories have been told about the *OCTOPUS* (OK-tuh-pus)! You have probably heard how it can pull a man down to its cave on the ocean floor. The fact of the matter is that the octopus and its relative, the *SQUID*, are very shy creatures. In order to frighten their enemies, they squirt a black, inky fluid and swim away.

The squid, like the octopus, has a head with distinct eyes and arms well equipped with powerful suckers. The main portion of the squid's body is long, while that of the octopi is round. The shell has become so reduced in size that it has become a rod inside the animals.

If you own a parakeet, you have probably given him a piece of the inside shell of the *CUTTLEFISH*—a relative of the squid. This soft shell gives the bird a place to sharpen his beak. It also supplies valuable minerals for good health.

LEARNED SO FAR

● Animals belonging to the mollusk phylum have shells and soft bodies.
● Examples of mollusks are clams, oysters, snails, octopus, and squid.
● Mollusks are an important source of man's food.

Self-Study Guide for Chapter 16

I. KNOWING AND UNDERSTANDING. FIND THE ANSWER. WRITE IT IN YOUR NOTEBOOK.

1. Members of the arthropod phylum can remain upright when removed from the water because
   a. they have eyes.
   b. they have outside skeletons.
   c. they have legs that may bend.
   d. they are advanced.

2. A horseshoe crab is known as a living fossil because
   a. it can be preserved.
   b. it is related to crabs.
   c. it is horseshoe-shaped.
   d. crabs today resemble fossil remains of years ago.
3. As the hermit crab grows larger, it is necessary for it to
   a. swim around.
   b. find another shell.
   c. live in deeper water.
   d. live in colder water.
4. Oysters and clams are related because they both have
   a. spiny skins.
   b. outside shells and soft bodies.
   c. tentacles.
   d. stinging cells.

II. FIND THE EXPLANATION. IN WHICH SECTION OF THE CHAPTER IS THE ANSWER TO EACH OF THE FOLLOWING QUESTIONS? WRITE THE QUESTION AND THE ANSWER IN YOUR NOTEBOOK.

1. Why are shrimps and crabs members of the arthropod phylum?
2. How do young lobsters undergo development?
3. How are pearls cultured in the Orient?

III. ON THE LADDER OF UNDERSTANDING. FILL IN THE CORRECT ANSWER IN YOUR NOTEBOOK.

1. The seaweeds are simple plants classified with the _____.
2. Seaweeds use _____ to make their own food.
3. The sponge body has many _____.
4. Jellyfish belong to the group of animals that have _____.

IV. STUDY THE DIAGRAM OF THE CLAM. ANSWER THE QUESTIONS BELOW IN YOUR NOTEBOOK.

1. The clam takes in water through its _____.
2. The movement of water is controlled by the beating of _____.
3. As the water passes over the gills, _____ is removed and _____ released.
4. Food is taken in when the water moves over the _____.

CHAPTER 17

Life in the Sea

PROBLEM:
*How are fish adapted
to their life in the sea?*

17–1 LOOKING BACK...

We saw (Section 15–1) that the phylum of chordates includes animals with some sort of backbone. Actually, some of these animals have simple rods made of *CARTILAGE* (KAR-tuh-lij) in their backs. Flip your outer ear, which is made of cartilage, and notice that it is flexible but returns to its shape and position. Other chordates that are more developed have spinal columns made of small bones called *VERTEBRAE* (VUR-tuh-bray). Run your hand across your own spine. The vertebrae are connected by cartilage. Your spine is flexible, but it keeps your body shape.

Fig. 137–1. Five classes of vertebrate skeletons. All are alike in one respect. What is it?

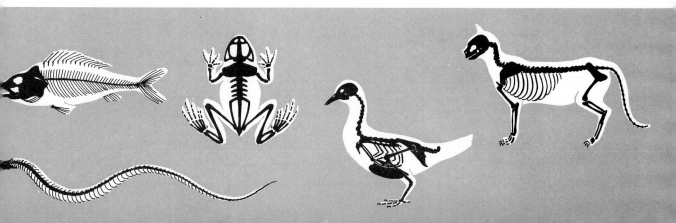

To many people, "a fish is a fish." To the marine biologist, fish are of many kinds. There are the primitive fish without jaws called *hagfish* and *lampreys*. There are fish whose bodies are mostly made of cartilage. These include the *sharks*, *rays*, and *skates*. Finally, there are the true *bony fish*.

Rays are interesting members of the shark family. They are flattened and have winglike fins. In the tropics, *stingrays* are the most feared creatures in the sea. The stingray has a sharp spine near the bottom of its tail. Special openings in the spine contain poison sacs. If a person steps on the spine, a powerful poison is released.

Rays live in waters close to shore, usually buried in the sand. *Skates* are harmless cousins of the rays. When you walk along the beach, you may find the skates' empty egg cases. They are sometimes called mermaid's purses. These leathery sacs enclose the embryo during its early development.

There are some bony fish that stay most of the time along the bottom and some that stay at middle depth. Others live near the surface and even come out of the water at times. One unusual fish is the common *flying fish*. These little fish glide out of the water on their winglike fins. Sometimes they can reach speeds up to 35 miles per hour.

FIG. 138–1. Skates and rays belong to the same group of fish. What characteristics do they have in common? The "mermaid's purse" encloses the skate's eggs. What type of fish is the skate?

To cope with the marine environment, fish have developed special adaptations.

Examine the picture of the fish in Fig. 139–1. How is it able to adapt to the problem of moving through the water? For one thing, it has a beautiful and streamlined shape. Since it is narrow at the head and tapers off toward the tail, the water can flow smoothly along its body.

The fins help the fish to move and steer. In some fish, like the *sea robin*, the fins have become adapted for crawling on the bottom. One fish can even crawl right out of the water! The flying fish uses its fins to glide over the water.

FIG. 139–1. How is the body of a fish modified for living in the water?

Fish don't drown because they can get dissolved oxygen from the water. Follow the process in Figure 139–2.

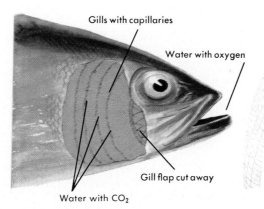

FIG. 139–2.
Water is taken in through the mouth. It passes over the gills, which are lined with many blood capillaries. Oxygen passes into the blood; carbon dioxide passes out of the blood. The water leaves through the gill slits under the gill flap.

Gills with capillaries

Water with oxygen

Gill flap cut away

Water with CO_2

- Fish are classified as vertebrates.
- Some fish have skeletons made up of cartilage; others have skeletons made of true bone.
- Fish have many adaptations that enable them to live in the watery world.

17–4 MEET THE SHARKS

Sharks are a very ancient group of vertebrates. They have changed little in 350 million years. The shark's body is very streamlined and fishlike.

The sharks have a reputation as killers of the sea. Any blood in the water can drive them into a feeding frenzy. Because of their fantastic powers of smell, sharks can detect wounded animals for miles around. Of the 250 shark species, only about 12 are believed to be really dangerous to humans.

The white shark is one of the most dangerous to humans. It can measure 30 feet or more. This shark is a very fast swimmer and has been known to attack humans. Another dangerous shark is the hammerhead. It has a very unusual head, shaped in the form of a T. The whale shark can reach a length of 50 feet but is really harmless. It feeds only on plankton.

FIG. 140–1. How does the shark differ from the bony fish illustrated in Figure 139–1?

17–5 LIFE CYCLE OF FISH

Reproduction is the most important process for continuing the species. Male and female members of most fish species shed their reproductive cells directly into the water. The male releases *sperm* (or *milt*). The female sheds *eggs* (or *roe*). Sperm and egg join in the process known as *fertilization*.

The young fish develop in the egg for a certain number of days. After hatching, they are called *FRY*. Not all the fertilized eggs will survive. Many are eaten by other fish. It has been estimated that a female codfish can lay 6 million eggs, but only 50,000 will ever become fry.

The eel, a slippery snakelike fish, is a good example with which to illustrate the fish's life cycle. When eels are between 5 and 8 years old, they make a journey to the Sargasso Sea. European eels also *migrate* to this area. The female then deposits her eggs; the male covers them with sperm. This is known as the *SPAWNING* process. Both parents then die. The fertilized eggs develop into the *larva* stage.

What happens to the larvae after hatching is a fascinating story. They begin a journey of thousands of miles that will take them back to the same rivers that were the homes of their parents. Both European and North American eels enter the Gulf Stream. In one to three years, they become adults.

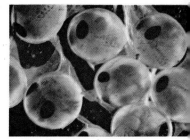

Fig. 141–1.
Fertilized eggs produce young, or *fry*.

Fig. 141–2.
Salmon may jump eight feet or more trying to clear an upstream rapids.

17–6 NATURE'S NAVIGATORS

Eel and salmon migrate, or change location, for spawning. How do they know where to go? How do they know where to return? Let's look at the salmon.

Adult salmon live in the Pacific Ocean. In the spring, they leave the ocean and enter the bays along the West Coast. They enter the Columbia River in Oregon. They fight their way upstream against the current and waterfalls. They spawn and the young fry hatch. They feed on plankton and develop. The parents die after spawning.

Some scientists believe the odors of the streams may guide the young fish back to the ocean. Some feel they follow currents. Can you think of some reasons why the migration takes place at all?

● Sharks are primitive fish with skeletons of cartilage.
● The life cycle of fish includes external development.
● Many fish migrate for their spawning process.

Self-Study Guide for Chapter 17

I. KNOWING AND UNDERSTANDING. FIND THE ANSWER. WRITE IT IN YOUR NOTEBOOK.

1. Fish are able to remove oxygen from the water because they have
   a. streamlined bodies.
   b. gills.
   c. good eyesight.
   d. fins.
2. Man and fish are placed in the same phylum because
   a. they both have vertebrae.
   b. they do not resemble one another.
   c. they lack backbones.
   d. they both have lungs.
3. The process following hatching is
   a. spawning.
   b. migration.
   c. fertilization.
   d. egg-laying.

II. WHICH IS THE OUTSIDER? CHOOSE THE ONE WORD IN THE LIST THAT DOES NOT BELONG WITH THE OTHERS. WRITE THE WORD.

1. Vertebrate, amphibian, fish, clam, bird.
2. Larvae, migration, eel, invertebrate.
3. Shark, cartilage, ray, bone.
4. Oxygen, gills, carbon dioxide, lung, fins.
5. Salmon, eel, bony fish, shark.

III. EXPLANATION, PLEASE.

1. How are fish adapted to life in the water?
2. What is the advantage of a fish producing so many eggs?
3. How is the Gulf Stream important in the life of the eel?

CHAPTER 18

Our Closest
Relatives
in the Sea

PROBLEM:
*What mammals live
in the sea?*

18-1 MORE VERTEBRATES IN THE SEA

The first class of vertebrates is that of the fish, just studied. A
second class, the *AMPHIBIANS* (am-FIB-ee-unz), includes
the frogs, toads, and salamanders. Amphibians spend part of
their lives in water, but they are truly land animals. They
breathe air through lungs.

The next class is the *REPTILES*, including snakes, turtles,
lizards, and alligators. There are a number of sea snakes. They
capture fish—often by poisoning them—and breathe air by
raising their nostrils out of the sea.

The sea is also the home of many huge turtles. They are
protected by shells, swim with giant flippers, and breathe air
through lungs. *Green turtles* and *loggerheads* grow to weigh
over 400 pounds. Turtles return to land to bury their eggs.
They then abandon the nests. The young, soon after hatching,
return to the sea.

18–2 MEET THE MAMMALS

Mammals are vertebrates whose females produce milk to feed their young. Most are covered by hair or fur. They have four-chambered hearts. This serves to keep them "warm blooded." In other words, they maintain a regular body temperature regardless of the temperature of the water or air.

Marine mammals include the whales, porpoises, dolphins, and seals. Other lesser-known creatures are the sea otter and manatee (MAN-uh-tee). These animals are amazing in their adaptation. They are fascinating for their size. Some show remarkable intelligence. All are economically useful to man.

18–3 *MOBY DICK*—THE STORY OF THE WHALES

The story of *Moby Dick* describes the adventures of Captain Ahab and his search to kill the famous white whale Moby Dick. In the end, the whale destroyed the ship and most of the men on board. This book was written in 1851, when whaling was a big industry in this country. Men would leave their homes for many months to hunt whales for food and oil.

When the lookout on board ship sighted a whale, he would shout, "thar she blows." What he saw was the whale's *SPOUT* (SPOWT), caused by blasts of air exhaled or blown out by the animal. A whale's spout sometimes reaches 20 feet into the air. Whalers could tell the type of whale by its spout. For example, some whales have a tall, thick spout; other spouts are divided in two at the top.

FIG. 144–1. Early whalers looked for the spouting of a whale. What causes the spouting?

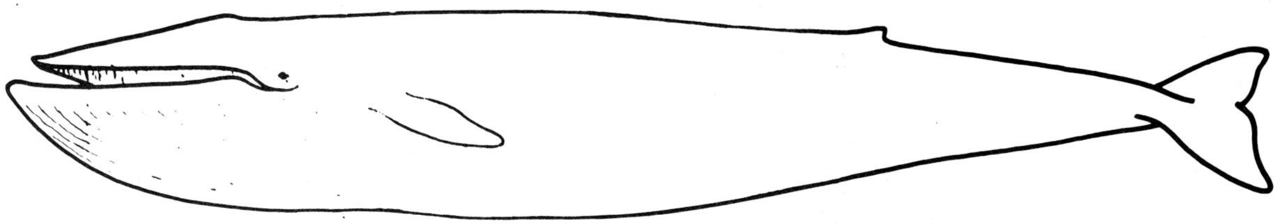

FIG. 145–1. Why do we classify the blue whale as a baleen whale?

Whales can be divided into two groups: toothless and toothed. BALEEN (bay-LEEN) are toothless whales.

Instead of teeth, the baleen whales have large mouths lined with a material called whalebone (baleen) that hangs from the upper jaw. The baleen acts as a strainer to capture tiny organisms from the sea. These whales feed mainly on tiny fish and a type of shrimplike plankton known as *KRILL*. Some of the largest whales belong to this group. The blue whale, for example, is one of the largest creatures that ever lived. It can grow to be 100 feet long and to weigh about 150 tons.

FIG. 145–2. Sperm whales dive to great depths in search of giant squid. What group of whales does it belong to?

The toothed whales (Figure 145–2) have teeth, which they use for capturing fish. One of the best-known toothed whales is the *SPERM WHALE*. It is the largest of these whales and grows to a length of about 60 feet. The sperm whale was hunted almost to extinction because its forehead contained a wax which was used as oil for lamps. It can dive to 3,000 feet for its favorite food, the giant squid.

What adaptations do whales have for life in the sea? To understand this, let's trace the whale back to its ancestors. Whales evolved to the watery world from extinct land mammals millions of years ago. One theory states that about 100 million years ago, small four-footed land animals entered the water. Over the course of time they developed torpedo-shaped bodies. The front legs developed into paddlelike fins. The hind legs developed into a structure called a *FLUKE*. The whale lost its covering of hair, and its nostrils moved to the top of its head to form the blowhole.

Examine the whale's skeleton in Figure 146–1. Does it resemble your own? The whale's fingers are covered by muscles which form a short fin. These fins help the whale in balance and movement. The bones in the fluke are the hind legs. To get movement, the whale fans its fluke up and down.

The whale's torpedo-like shape and smooth surface help him to get through the water quickly. Under his skin, he has thick layers of oil-rich *blubber* or fat. This layer protects the whale when he travels into the cold Arctic and Antarctic seas. It also helps him to maintain his body temperature.

Whales, like other mammals, are warm-blooded; that is, their body temperature remains even. They maintain the same temperature because of their powerful four-chambered hearts. We learned before that whales have lungs. Air is taken in through the blowhole.

Scientists are studying whales to learn how they can hold their breath for long periods of time. How can they dive so deep and rise to the surface so quickly? Sperm whales, for example, can stay under water for more than an hour.

Fig. 146–1.
The whale's skeleton is similar to your own. How is the whale adapted to life in the water?

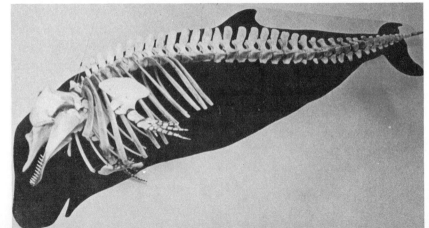

- Whales, dolphins, porpoises, and seals belong to the mammal group.
- Whales are warm-blooded, air-breathing creatures beautifully adapted to the water.
- Whales evolved from creatures that once lived on land.

18–5 VANISHING WHALES: A CALL FOR CONSERVATION

We learned in Section 18–3 that years ago men hunted whales for their oil and meat. Whaling continued into this century, but the methods used were different. Instead of going after the whales in small boats, men began to use radar and helicopters. Once a whale is located, a special gun shoots a harpoon containing an explosive charge at it. As a result of these methods, whales have continued to decline in numbers. For example, in the first part of this century, there were 100,000 blue whales in Antarctica. Scientists estimate that today there may be only a few hundred left.

Despite the fact that many whales are on the road to extinction, some countries still continue to hunt them. These countries use the oil for soap, fertilizers, and ink, and the meat for pet foods.

Conservationists are urging the adoption of laws and international controls to save the whales from extinction.

18–6 DOLPHINS AND PORPOISES: BRAIN AND BRAWN

From early Roman times comes the story of a *dolphin* that made friends with a young boy. The dolphin would carry the boy on its back wherever he went. Throughout history there have been reports of how dolphins have saved swimmers from sharks. Are these stories real or just legend? Scientists have made many studies of these creatures. They will admit that the dolphin is quite intelligent. Perhaps even intelligent enough to carry a boy on its back!

Fig. 147–1. Porpoises are extremely intelligent creatures. What group of whales do they belong to?

Just what is a dolphin? What is a porpoise? Many times these words are used to describe the same animal. Both dolphins and porpoises belong to the toothed-whale family. An easy way to tell the difference between a porpoise and a dolphin is by the fact that the porpoise does not have the "grin" on its face. The dolphin has a snout which is shaped into a beak.

The bottle-nosed porpoise is the one most often seen in captivity. When full size, it may reach a length of 8 feet and may weigh 800 pounds. These animals also have a wonderful communication system. They can signal each other with sounds and body movements. Because of their intelligence, bottle-noses have been used by the Navy. A porpoise named *Tuffy* was trained to deliver tools and messages to divers living under water in a special project called *SEALAB*. It is hoped that someday dolphins will be able to work alongside divers.

Dolphins and porpoises are being studied for their remarkable sonar systems. (Review SONAR, figure 29–1.) They send out their own sound in the form of high-pitched squeaks. They then wait for the echo to return. Porpoises have even been trained to jump through hoops blindfolded!

Fig. 148–1. Bottle-nosed porpoises are the animals most often found in aquariums.

18–7 MORE MARINE MAMMALS

The seals, walruses, sea otters, and sea cows are also important to life. Figure 148–2 shows a sea cow. It belongs to the order of mammals known as *Carnivora*. All carnivores have special teeth adapted to eating meat. Seals and walruses are excellent swimmers that feed on fish. Their legs, like the whale's, are adapted for life in the water.

Sea otters are amusing little creatures that like to swim on their backs. They are found along the Pacific Coast from Alaska to California. They hunt for *ABALONE* (ab-uh-LOH-nee), a mollusk, in kelp beds off Southern California. Their fur is very fine and they were once hunted for it. Since they were almost wiped out, they are now protected by many governments.

Fig. 148–2. Sea cows or *MANATEES* (MAN-uh-teez) are large, gentle sea mammals that feed on water plants along the Florida coasts.

● Conservation is needed to protect the vanishing whales and otters.
● Dolphins and porpoises are intelligent sea mammals belonging to the toothed-whale family.
● Other sea mammals include seals, walruses, sea otters, and sea cows.

Self-Study Guide for Chapter 18

I. KNOWING AND UNDERSTANDING. FIND THE ANSWER. WRITE IT IN YOUR NOTEBOOK.

1. Sea mammals belong to the higher group of animals known as
   a. mollusks.
   b. invertebrates.
   c. vertebrates.
   d. crustaceans.
2. One adaptation that all whales have for life in the water is
   a. gills.
   b. hind legs in the form of a fluke.
   c. thin skin.
   d. scales.
3. Baleen whales are adapted to feed on
   a. fish.
   b. plankton.
   c. other whales.
   d. seals.
4. One adaptation of whales for living in cold Arctic seas is their
   a. thick, oil-rich blubber.
   b. blowholes.
   c. small eyes.
   d. flukes.

II. WHAT'S THE DIFFERENCE? STATE THE DIFFERENCE CLEARLY IN YOUR OWN WORDS.

1. What is the difference between a whale's spout and its lungs?
2. What is the difference between a dolphin and a porpoise?
3. What is the difference between a baleen and a toothed whale?
4. What is the difference between a mammal and a fish?

CHAPTER 19

Salt Marshes— Nurseries of the Sea

PROBLEM:
Why should we protect our salt marshes?

19–1 A NURSERY FOR LIFE

What does a salt marsh mean to most people? Is it a place to fill in with garbage? Is it, perhaps, a good site for a housing community or an airport? Maybe you thought of it as an area with some overgrown grass and smelly mud.

The marine biologist knows it is a *nursery for life*. Here, in the shallow and protected waters of the marsh, game fish and crustaceans spend their early lives. When they are large enough, they will move out to the unprotected waters of a bay or estuary. Here, too, is the home of shore birds who nest, lay eggs, and "bring up their families."

FIG. 150–1. A salt marsh—a true study in ecology.

19-2 WETLANDS AND MARSHLANDS

A new word has appeared in newspapers and magazines: *WET-LANDS*. Wetlands are the shores near our oceans. They consist of shallow saltwater pools, called *marshes*, together with soft, mud beaches near them and around them. Wetlands have become the focus of many environmental organizations. They have even called forth new laws. Why? First, let us learn the characteristics of the marsh.

19-3 BIRTH AND GROWTH OF A MARSH

Salt marshes are found near sheltered ocean waters, usually in places where rivers or bays enter the sea.

Some of the best-known marshes in the United States are found along its eastern coast. Some states feel they are so important to the ecology that they have preserved them forever. New York State, with many acres of wetlands, recently passed a wetlands protection bill.

FIG. 151-1. The "big birds" at Kennedy International Airport are not good for the health of shrimps, shellfish, birds, or fish. How can planning prevent destruction of life in the marshes?

FIG. 152–1. Tidal creeks divide marshlands into little islands. Why are the creeks brackish? What else is in the mud?

As the tides sweep in, the water floods the shore. When the tide retreats, the land is left muddy. In the summer, it is baked by the hot sun; in the winter, it is chilled by cold winds and cold waves.

From inland, fresh water from estuaries enters the shallow marshes. Heavy rains and snow also add fresh water. The result is that marsh water is not quite so salty as the sea. It is really brackish. The low portion of the marsh ends in a mud beach or mud flat. In many places, *TIDAL CREEKS* divide the marshlands into little islands. Mud flats are thought to rise about an inch a year.

If we were to examine the mud, we would find that it contains much *PEAT* (decomposed organic material). Here is a marvelous example of nature's cycling: dead animals and dead plants are returned to the soil to be used as food once again by other living things.

Perhaps this is the meaning of the Old Testament quotation: "Dust thou art; unto dust shalt thou return."

19–4 SALT MARSH ZONES

The salt marsh can be divided into zones of life. The zones result from abiotic factors such as salinity, temperature, type of soil, and distance above high-tide level. Animals and plants living here have adapted to these conditions over thousands of years.

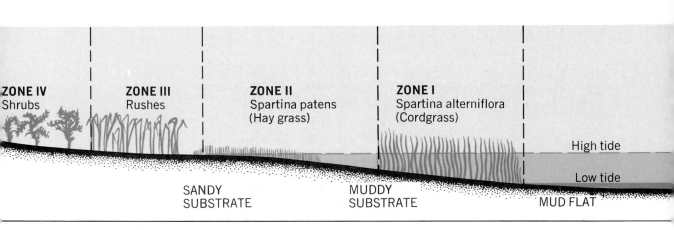

FIG. 153–1. The salt marsh shows zonation. Why do we find different plants in each zone?

19–5 MUD FLATS—GATEWAYS TO THE MARSH

A good place to look for mud flats is near a quiet bay or estuary. You will quickly notice the softness of the mud. Since there is little wave action, mud particles are held close together, resulting in little exchange of gases. You may also smell the odor of rotten eggs. This is caused by certain bacteria living in the deeper layers of the mud. This bacterial action decomposes organic matter to release *hydrogen sulfide*, which has a rotten-egg odor. These bacteria can live without oxygen.

FIG. 153–2. High tide sweeps in twice daily. It brings fresh oxygen into the pools and churns up the decayed nutrients. Fish swim in with the tide. When the tides drop low, they carry nutrients out to the sea to feed marine animals. Dead crustaceans and dead fish left by the tide are food for marsh birds.

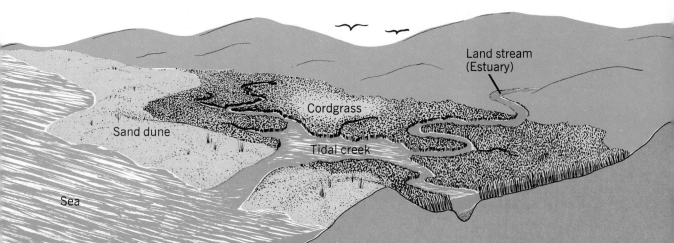

- Wetlands are marshlands of mud flats and tidal creeks.
- Salt marshes are thought of as "nurseries of the sea."
- Marshes show distinct zones of life.
- Food and game fish spend a good part of their lives in the marsh.

19–6   PLANT ZONES OF THE MARSH

The marsh begins where the mud cliffs rise gently from the flats. These cliffs may be dotted with the *BURROWS* (BUR-roze) of fiddler crabs. Great numbers of these crustaceans can be found throughout the marsh.

Just above the mud cliff is a thick, overgrown zone of salt-marsh plants called *CORDGRASS*. This hardy plant species grows much taller near the water. Cordgrass is actually a land plant which has become adapted to living in salty areas. Can you think of one problem it faces in a saltwater environment?

It can reach a height of 6 feet. In a healthy, unpolluted marsh area, an acre of land can produce an average of 5 tons of cordgrass! Some of the grass-blades are eaten by the animals that inhabit the marsh. About half the grass decays and floats into the estuaries. It forms food for the marine animals.

Farther in, on the higher elevations of the marsh, grows another type of grass called *SALT HAY GRASS*. This is a thinner and shorter species. It grows where only the highest tides

FIG. 154–1. This photo shows the edge of a mud bank.

Fig. 155–1. Spartina (cord) grass is able to live in the brackish environment of the salt marsh. What problems does it face here?

reach, in less salty, more sandy land. Salt hay grass is harvested by farmers. It is used to cover farm plants to keep them moist (as a *mulch*).

Beyond the point of the highest tide levels, the marsh turns toward the land. The soil becomes sandy. The main types of plants are bushes and shrubs.

19–7 ANIMALS OF THE MARSH

Many forms of animal life can be found living in close association with the plants. The tall spartina (cord) grass bordering the marsh creeks is a good place to look. Among the animals you may notice are these:

Mud snails. When the tide is out, thousands of these tiny creatures may be seen feeding on the surface.

Crabs. Blue crabs hide in the mud, and little fiddler crabs are found everywhere. At low tide, the fiddler feeds on dead plant and animal material.

Mussels. Bits of their shells may be seen sticking up out of the mud. They are called RIBBED mussels because their shells are covered with tiny lines. At high tide, mussels open their shells slightly to feed on particles in the water. They act as tiny filters that clean the marsh.

Bloodworms and sandworms. These worms are found just below the mud surface. They are the bait used in commercial fishing.

At high tide, many areas of the marsh become flooded with the onrushing water. Young fish now move higher into the marsh to seek protection among the plants.

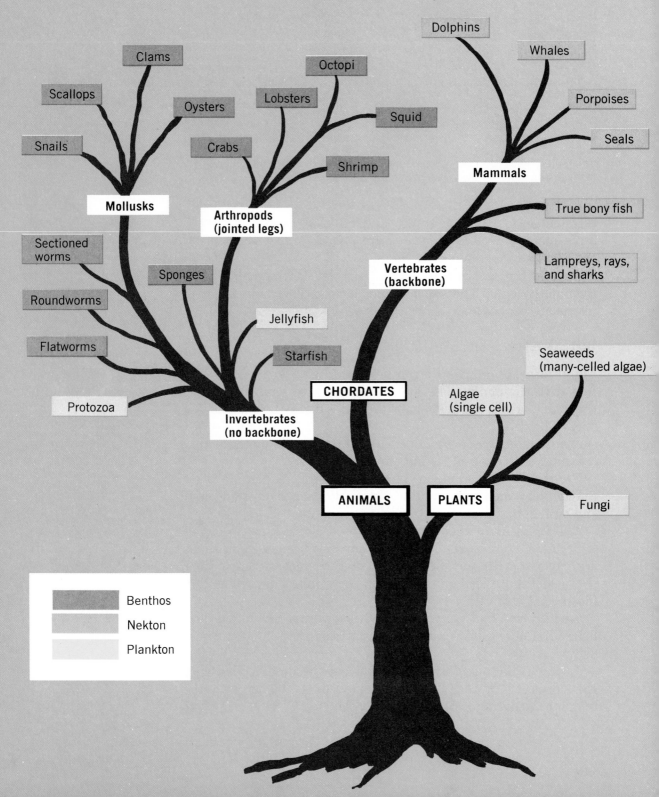

Tree of Marine Life

Dolphins

Whales

Porpoises

Seals

Clams

Octopi

Lobsters

Scallops

Oysters

Squid

Snails

Crabs

Shrimp

Mammals

Mollusks

Arthropods (jointed legs)

True bony fish

Sectioned worms

Sponges

Vertebrates (backbone)

Roundworms

Lampreys, rays, and sharks

Jellyfish

Flatworms

Starfish

Seaweeds (many-celled algae)

Protozoa

CHORDATES

Algae (single cell)

Invertebrates (no backbone)

ANIMALS   **PLANTS**

Fungi

Benthos

Nekton

Plankton

COMMON RESIDENTS IN WETLANDS

BIRDS
{
Duck
White ibis
Laughing gull
Osprey
Snowy egret
Marsh wren
Sandpiper
}

MOLLUSKS
{
Clam
Oyster
Ribbed mussel
}

MAMMALS
{
Raccoon
Mink
Otter
}

INSECTS
{
Grasshopper
Cricket
}

CRUSTACEANS
{
Barnacle
Blue crab
Fiddler crab
Shrimp
}

WORMS
{
Bloodworm
Sandworm
}

GRASSES
{
Cordgrass
Hay grass
}

FISH
{
Mullet
Spadefish
Anchovy
Flounder
Goby
Killie
Menhaden
}

LEARNED SO FAR

● Great numbers of animals live in close association with the plants.
● Since marshes are so important, they must be preserved.

Self-Study Guide for Chapter 19

I. KNOWING AND UNDERSTANDING. FIND THE ANSWER. WRITE IT IN YOUR NOTEBOOK.

1. The water in marsh creeks is usually brackish because
   a. there is a high evaporation rate.
   b. fresh water mixes with the salt.
   c. of high temperatures.
   d. of polluted waters.
2. Peat results from the breakdown of
   a. dead plants and animals.
   b. rainwater.
   c. seawater.
   d. marsh mud.

3. Because there is no oxygen in the mud flat, animals living in the mud must
   a. move to the surface.
   b. extend their tubes to the surface.
   c. dig into the mud.
   d. slow down their breathing.

II. EXPLANATION, PLEASE.

1. How do marshes provide homes for animal life?
2. Why does the marsh mud have a rotten-egg odor?
3. Why do we call a marsh a wetland?
4. What factors determine the zonation in the marsh?

III. TRUE OR FALSE? WRITE THE FOLLOWING STATEMENTS IN YOUR NOTEBOOK. IF THE CAPITALIZED WORD IS CORRECT, WRITE TRUE. IF THE CAPITALIZED WORD IS FALSE, WRITE THE WORD THAT WILL MAKE THE STATEMENT TRUE.

1. A marsh is sometimes called a NURSERY for life.
2. One crab that can be found throughout the marsh in great numbers is the FIDDLER CRAB.
3. RIBBED MUSSELS act as tiny filters in the marsh mud.

IV. FOR THE HOME SCIENTIST.

INVESTIGATION: What problem does a plant face in a saltwater environment?

PROCEDURES
1. Lettuce is actually the leaf of a plant. Take a fresh lettuce leaf and place it in a strong salt solution overnight.
2. Place an equal-sized leaf in unsalted water.
3. The following morning, remove the leaves and compare them.

OBSERVATIONS AND ANALYSIS
1. What happened to the two leaves? Explain.
2. How might cordgrass survive in the saltwater environment?
3. What was the purpose of step 2 in the procedures?

UNIT IV

The Use and Misuse of Our Oceans

WHAT'S IT ALL ABOUT?

In our first three UNITS, we learned about the nature of the ocean, how it is studied, and about life in the sea.

Probably the most important idea you have gotten is that there is a delicate balance in the oceans. There is a balance between living things and the marine environment. There is also a balance among the living things.

Along come human beings, the most intelligent animal. Through their industrial developments, through carelessness, and through ignorance they have dumped foreign matter into the oceans. They have upset the balance of life in the sea.

In addition, humans are big "takers." They have overfished, overkilled, and overcollected the ocean's products. Again, the balance has been upset. Some living species may actually be disappearing!

In this UNIT, we shall study the causes of ocean pollution and our program to stop it. We shall sum up the story of the wonderful "treasures" of the ocean now and in the future. We shall explore methods to use these ocean resources wisely.

FIG. 159–1.

CHAPTER 20

Pollution
Destroys

PROBLEM:
Why is pollution of the oceans a serious problem?

20–1 FOULING UP OUR OCEANS

It's beautiful . . . clear . . . fresh . . . blue . . . sparkling green. These are words we could, in the past, almost always use about our oceans. Not any more!

Your favorite beach may now (or soon) have a warning sign posted saying NO SWIMMING.

We are also destroying the salt marshes at an alarming rate. By dumping wastes into the waterways, we pollute them. Builders fill marshes to build housing communities and factories.

How do we prevent their destruction? Government and citizens must pass laws to stop this. People must be educated. In this way, we may conserve what is left.

20–2 SOURCES OF POLLUTION

What is a polluted body of water? Any substance found in water in great quantities may be termed a *POLLUTANT* (puh-LOOT-unt). To understand the effects of pollutants on our marine environment, we shall study the estuary, which is very sensitive to changes. Since it is also a nursery for the sea, any harm done here can affect the life of the sea.

Polluted water is, therefore, any water whose contents may affect the natural plant and animal life within it. Indirectly, it may also have an ill effect on those animals who get food from the sea. Of course, this includes human beings.

Did you know that the Pacific Ocean contains ten times the natural level of lead? Where does it come from? From the exhaust gases of automobiles using leaded gasoline. Here is only one example of how our "harmless" activity can pollute our waters.

The chart below shows where water pollutants come from.

TYPICAL WATER POLLUTANTS

Pesticides: DDT, 2-4D
Radioactive materials:
   radium-226, strontium 90
Chemicals: acids, ammonia,
   arsenic chlorides, phosphates, dyes, hydrogen
   sulfide, lead, mercury,
   nitrates, tars, urea, zinc

SOLID WASTES

Paper	46%	
Garbage	12%	
Glass, etc.	10%	
Grass, dirt	10%	3.5 billion tons per year in the United States
Metals	8%	
Wood	7%	
Miscellaneous	7%	

Source: U.S. Public Health Service

20–3 POLLUTANTS MOVE IN

- From the waters of the estuaries.
- From fallout of particles from the air.
- As wash-down with rain and snow.
- When dumped by humans.
- When carried by polluted animals from other seas.
- When carried by currents.

Fig. 161–1. Is it necessary to curb these practices completely to stop pollution? Explain your answer.

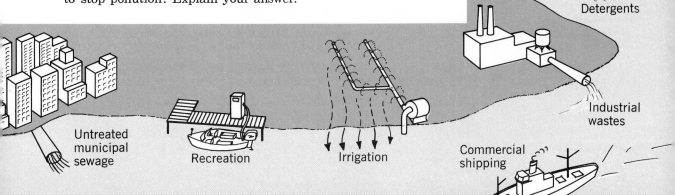

Decaying vegetation, aquatic plants

Detergents

Untreated municipal sewage

Recreation

Irrigation

Commercial shipping

Industrial wastes

20–4 THE WASTE PROBLEM

Have you ever wondered what happens to waste after it leaves your home? A good portion of it is treated to make it less dangerous. Some of it enters streams, rivers, and seas in the form of raw waste. We call these products *SEWAGE* (SOO-ij). It has been estimated that every second, 2 million gallons of sewage are dumped into the waterways of our country.

FIG. 162–1. *A.* Raw sewage is pouring out of the pipe at the left. *B.* The boat at the right is carrying *SLUDGE* (SLUJ), which is a by-product of sewage treatment. How do these two actions affect the marine biome?

FIG. 162–2. These fish died from lack of oxygen. What could have caused such a low level of oxygen?

In a natural setting, organic sewage is decomposed by bacteria. Such materials are called *BIODEGRADABLE* (BY-o-dee-GRAY-duh-bul). (This big word should not scare anyone: *bio* = "life"; *degrade* = "to break down"; *able* = "able." Therefore, "able to be broken down by life processes.")

Unfortunately, much of our waste is not biodegradable. The phosphates in detergents are not; neither are most plastics, neither is the aluminum nor iron in food cans, and neither is glass.

20–5 A BACTERIAL EXPLOSION

Sewage contains large amounts of complex organic chemicals. These provide food for many types of bacteria which live in the water. The bacteria in turn break down these substances into simple forms. This process is known as *DECOMPOSITION* (dee-kom-puh-ZISH-un). For this process, bacteria require large amounts of oxygen. This "steals" the oxygen from plants, fish, and other higher forms of life.

Untreated sewage is very dangerous because it may contain harmful microorganisms such as bacteria and *VIRUSES* (VY-ruh-sez). The person who swims in this water takes the chance of absorbing these germs into his body. Eating clams from polluted water can cause a liver disease known as *HEPATITIS* (hep-uh-TY-tus). Clams and other mollusks can concentrate these harmful germs in their bodies. Then they pass them on to people who eat them uncooked.

20–6 PHOSPHATES: WHEN MORE IS NOT BETTER

Next time you're at the supermarket, look at the label on a box of household detergent. It will probably say, "CONTAINS NO PHOSPHATE." Until recently, many detergents contained phosphates, which dissolved dirt in clothes.

Phosphates were dumped into the water through sewage outlets. Once in the estuary, they could not dissolve. Instead, they were used by the water plants as food. They acted as *FERTILIZERS* (FUR-tuh-ly-zurz)! As a result, plankton and other plants increased in great numbers. The estuaries became choked with plants. Other plants growing in deeper waters could not get the light they needed for growth. These plants then died and were decomposed by bacteria. Again, the supply of oxygen was down. Fish and other marine life began to die.

Can you see why this has sometimes been called the cycle of death? No wonder some communities passed laws against phosphates in detergents!

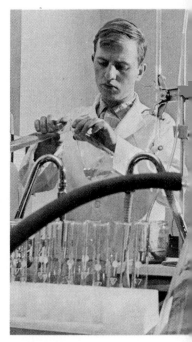

Fig. 163–1. Scientists perform chemical and bacterial-culture tests to study polluted water.

LEARNED SO FAR

- Our oceans and estuaries are being polluted.
- Pollution endangers the ecological cycle.
- Pollution may cause disease and death.
- Pollution comes from many human sources.

Fɪɢ. 164-1.
What would be some
ways to ensure that the
osprey survives?

20–7   A MIRACLE CHEMICAL BRINGS A CURSE

Sewage alone can destroy waterways. But another problem is the widespread use of *PESTICIDES* (PES-tuh-sides) — chemicals used to kill insects.

DDT, discovered during World War II, was hailed as the "miracle mosquito killer." For example, Puerto Rico's malaria mosquitoes were wiped out by DDT. But, the miracle was also a curse, for DDT was being passed through the food web to other animals. Furthermore, it did not break down into harmless substances, remaining active and destructive.

In order to kill mosquitoes, large amounts of DDT were sprayed over the salt marshes—but many fish and birds were also destroyed. An example is the *OSPREY* (OS-pray), a large fish-eating bird. DDT interferes with the formation of normal eggshells in female birds. The eggs crack easily, and being exposed to the air before they are ready to hatch, young birds never reach the hatching stage.

20–8   HEATING UP THE WATERS

To cool their generators, electric power plants need water. This is also true of many other factories and atomic energy plants. The water is taken from an estuary or bay, circulated through pipes, and returned at a higher temperature. The heated water may interfere with life cycles in the water. This is called *THERMAL* (THUR-mul) pollution.

Scientists know that heated water may be harmful to marine life. Fish that ordinarily migrate when cold weather approaches may remain near the warm-water outlet pipe. If for any reason the plant is suddenly shut down, the fish would be exposed to sudden cold. In recent years, many fish kills were caused by plant shutdowns.

20–9   OIL SPILLS

You have probably heard the expression "oil and water do not mix." In March, 1967, the oil tanker *Torrey Canyon* crashed onto the rocks off the English coast. Most of her 36 millon gallons of oil poured into the sea. This is just another example of how people pollute the sea.

The oil and water did not mix; the oil did not sink or dissolve. As a result, many plants stopped producing oxygen because they could not get the light they needed. Many small animals were poisoned when the oil entered their bodies. Feathers of many sea birds became coated. They could not fly. Some floated on the water and then drowned.

20-10 WATER POLLUTION TRAVELS FAR

In October, 1970, newspapers reported that the livers of Alaskan fur seals showed traces of mercury. Yet these seals live from 50 to 1,000 miles from land! The Alaskans in that area were immediately warned not to eat seal livers. Mercury in humans can damage the brain.

Where had the mercury come from? One guess is that seals migrate along our Pacific Coast. The same factories that make paper and pulp dump waste into the ocean. Mercury is one such waste.

As you learned before, marine life forms a food chain. The mercury may have moved from plankton to fish like salmon and pollock and into the livers of fur seals—link to link!

The Food and Drug Administration ordered that vitamin pills made from seal livers be removed from the market.

From this, you can certainly see how far pollution can travel. Is there any place on earth that cannot become polluted?

20-11 CLEANING OUR FOUL WATERS

Well, we know some of the causes. We know some of the effects. What can we do? The quickest solution is to stop polluting. But this is not so easy when people produce more garbage and wastes than the water can safely hold. We must find ways of treating these wastes so that they will not be harmful to our waterways. The answers require much cooperation, much scientific research, and lots and lots of money.

We need new kinds of detergents. Industry must find new cooling methods for its waste water. New sewage treatment techniques must be developed. We must find new ways to dispose of solid waste. Certainly, we must cut down on the use of nonbiodegradable materials.

Our antipollution program has just begun.

LEARNED SO FAR

- Chemicals and oil can travel through the food web and cause death in animals and plants.
- Heating the waters may have long-range effects on the ecology.
- Pollutants can be transferred from the simplest to the most complex organisms.

Self-Study Guide for Chapter 20

I. KNOWING AND UNDERSTANDING. FIND THE ANSWER. WRITE IT IN YOUR NOTEBOOK.

1. One problem that arises when bacteria receive large amounts of organic chemicals is that
   a. they need large amounts of oxygen to carry out decomposition.
   b. they die from lack of oxygen.
   c. they can't get enough food.
   d. they move to other areas.
2. When phosphates are added to water, they cause plants to grow rapidly. The result is that
   a. fish have plenty of food.
   b. the plants die; the oxygen in the water is used up.
   c. the plants provide hiding places for small animals.
   d. more oxygen is released.

II. EXPLANATION, PLEASE.

1. What do we mean by a pollutant?
2. How can pollutants enter an area?
3. How can untreated sewage be dangerous to man?
4. How has DDT interfered with the life cycle of the animals?

III. MATCH THE WORDS IN COLUMN *A* WITH THOSE IN COLUMN *B*. WRITE ONLY IN YOUR NOTEBOOK.

A	*B*
1. Hepatitis	a. Results from oil spill
2. Decomposition	b. Release of heated water
3. Pesticide	c. May contain phosphates
4. Osprey	d. May result from eating clams
5. Thermal pollution	e. Breakdown of substances
6. Detergents	f. DDT
	g. Decline due to pesticide
	h. Adds oxygen to water

IV. FOR THE HOME SCIENTIST.

INVESTIGATION: What effect does a phosphate detergent have upon plant growth?

PROCEDURES

1. At a pond or ditch, collect some water containing algae. The algae will appear as a green covering on the surface of the pond. You may also substitute some freshwater plants purchased at your pet shop.
2. Fill three jars with the pond water. Label them 1, 2, and 3. Place 2 tablespoons of a high-phosphate detergent in jar 1. In jar 2, place 2 tablespoons of a nonphosphate detergent. Jar 3 contains plain pond water.
3. Place the jars in a warm, lighted area. Observe daily.

OBSERVATIONS AND ANALYSIS

1. In which jars did the plants grow best? Explain your answer.
2. Explain what would happen if high-phosphate detergents were added to our waterways.
3. Draw a simple diagram to show this investigation. Label all parts.

CHAPTER 21

Our Oceans: Our Future

PROBLEM:
How can the wise use of our oceans make a better future for us?

21-1 USE IT...BUT WISELY

As you saw in Chapter 20, we have misused the ocean. But our biosphere includes the ocean. We are "entitled" to use it.

In this chapter, we shall look back to what oceanographers have learned. You will see that the ocean has gifts to give us. There are gifts of food, minerals, jewelry, and fur. There are gifts of energy. Most important, the waters of the ocean may be the greatest gift of all.

We have come to our last chapter. But this is not the end of the story. For the ocean around us may truly control our future.

Modern oceanography is even carrying out research to see whether humans can live below the water in a new habitat.

FIG. 168–1. The *Sea Lab* is an ocean exploring vessel in which scientists lived below the water.

FIG. 168–2. The *Tektite* projects, staffed by women aquanauts, operated below the waters near the United States Virgin Islands in 1970 for 60 days. What are some problems in underwater habitats?

21-2 FISH IN OUR FUTURE

How long will the oceans of the world continue to supply us with a rich harvest? Unless wise conservation practices are adopted immediately, we may not have "fish in our future." Fishery biologists need to understand the life cycles and factors in the environment that affect food fish. To learn where different fish migrate, scientists attach tags to the fish. A reward is offered to anyone who returns the tag. The scientists are interested in where the fish was caught and how big it was. This method also helps to understand growth rates and ages. Through their tagging operations, they can also learn where the new fishing grounds are located.

What methods can we now use to protect our available stocks?

FIG. 169–1.
Fish are tagged to learn more about where they migrate. How does this help the biologist conserve valuable fish?

21-3 NETTING A GOOD CATCH

How long will the sea continue to supply us with our food fish? Many fishing countries throughout the world are employing the methods of science to help them catch fish. They are so successful that large stocks of our food fish are not as plentiful as they once were. Large fleets are stationed off the continental shelves, harvesting food fish such as flounder, cod, and bluefish. The United States ranks fifth in world fishing nations. The chart below shows some interesting statistics about fish.

FIG. 169–2.

FACTS, FIGURES, AND FISH

Rank in Size of Catch	Major Fishing Grounds Near	Most Abundant Fish
1. Japan	British Isles	Herrings
2. Peru	Iceland	Anchovies
3. Soviet Union	Norway	Sardines
4. China	Soviet Union	Pilchards
5. United States	Newfoundland	Menhaden

Fig. 170–1.
A fish factory at sea. What are the advantages of fish processing at sea?

Fig. 170–2.
Grinding trash fish to make FPC. Wheat bread containing 5 percent FPC can give starving nations all the protein needed in a daily diet.

21–4   NEW FISHING METHODS

Modern fishing fleets consist of *spotters, catchers,* and *fish factory ships.* The spotters locate the fish, using airplanes and echo sounders.

A still newer method uses lights and electricity. The light and electric currents are sent into the water on a large tube. The light attracts the fish and they move toward an electric current. A powerful pump then scoops the fish up to the ship.

After the fish are located and trapped, they are brought to a factory ship. Here they will be cleaned and canned or frozen. The packed fish can even be sent to port while the fleet continues to work.

21–5   TRASH FISH

Not all fish taste good in the usual fish dinner. But scientists tell us that by throwing away such fish we may be wasting valuable protein. Such "trash fish" can be ground into *FISH PROTEIN CONCENTRATE,* or FPC. It forms a white powder and can even be mixed with flour to make bread. Our government now permits the common menhaden and herring to be used in FPC manufacture.

Trash fish are also used to make other fish products: fertilizer, oil for paints, varnish. A very common fish used for this is the Atlantic *MENHADEN* (men-HAY-dun), a relative of the common herring.

LEARNED SO FAR

- New research is studying the ability of humans to live under water.
- Fish may become more and more important in the future.
- Old and new fishing methods are combined to bring in our catch.
- Different fishing methods are used for different ocean levels.
- Some fish, not good for ordinary eating, are the source of valuable fish products.

21–6 SEA RANCHING

Sea farming is known as *MARICULTURE*. (*Aquaculture* concerns the raising of both freshwater and saltwater animals.) Let's say that you were thinking of starting a ranch of your own. What part of the sea would you use? What equipment would you need? Ask the Japanese! They have been farming the sea for many years.

The best area to set up such a farm would be a shallow bay or estuary. It must be in a place that is protected from strong waves but yet be able to receive a food supply with the incoming tide. What food supplies would you depend upon?

What animal would you try to raise? The Japanese have been successful with eels, shrimp, oysters, seaweeds, octopi, and fish.

Fig. 171–1.
Oysters can be raised near the warm water outlets of power plants. How is this beneficial to the oyster's growth?

21–7 WATER, WATER EVERYWHERE...

Yes, so much water—but not fit to drink. Why not? Of course ... the salt and other dissolved minerals would affect the blood and other body fluids. Violent cramps and death can follow the drinking of seawater.

Scientists have now found some methods for removing the salt. This is the process of *DESALINATION* (dee-sal-uh-NAY-shun). Three methods are in use.

DISTILLATION (dis-ti-LAY-shun)	Evaporating the water with high heat, then condensing it by cooling
FILTRATION (fil-TRAY-shun)	Filtering the water through special membranes
CRYSTALLIZATION (kris-tuh-li-ZAY-shun)	Freezing the water and removing the ice crystals

Fig. 171–2.
Desalination is a costly process. Why?

The most successful method now used is distillation. This produces 98 percent of the water now taken from the sea. This process requires large amounts of heat. Some desalination plants are now using atomic energy.

21–8 MINERALS FROM THE SEA

The chemist may think of the sea as a "gold mine." Great deposits of valuable chemicals can be found there. Of special interest is the metal *MANGANESE* (MAN-guh-neez). Using special underwater cameras, scientists have photographed large deposits known as *NODULES* (NOD-yoolz).

The sea has many minerals to offer us. But if you're thinking of gold, you're too hopeful. At this time, the only minerals being taken directly from seawater are salt (sodium chloride), magnesium, and bromine. Most magnesium in the United States now comes from seawater. The manganese nodules are still not profitable. Iodine and bromine are also removed from seaweeds. Sand, gravel, and sulfur are other useful sea products. Japan digs almost a third of its coal from beneath the ocean, while Britain gets about 10 percent of its coal from below the sea.

21–9 OIL AND GAS FROM THE OCEAN

The sea also contains large deposits of petroleum oil used to manufacture gasoline. Oil is brought to the surface from the sediments below. Drilling in shallow water is done from permanent platforms called "Texas towers." In deeper water, special oil-drilling ships are sent out to the site. This oil is concentrated in the continental shelf. We are now removing 16 percent of our oil from beneath the ocean. Most natural oil is in the Persian Gulf and in the Gulf of Mexico, off the shore of Louisiana.

Natural gas, which is largely methane (CH_4), is often found with offshore petroleum. It makes up about 6 percent of the natural gas used for cooking in American homes.

FIG. 172–1.
A dense concentration of manganese nodules. Why would these chemicals be difficult to mine?

FIG. 172–2.
An oil rig removes oil from beneath the sea.

LEARNED SO FAR

- Sea ranching is an industry that raises marine animals with artificial controls.
- Desalination produces fresh water from seawater by three methods.
- The sea is a source of many useful minerals and fuels.

Self-Study Guide for Chapter 21

I. KNOWING AND UNDERSTANDING. FIND THE ANSWER. WRITE IT IN YOUR NOTEBOOK.

1. By throwing away fish that are not eaten by us, we may be wasting a valuable source of
   a. sugar.
   b. protein.
   c. fertilizer.
   d. animal feed.
2. To prevent a drop in our fish populations, we must
   a. modernize our fishing fleets.
   b. learn more about fish behavior.
   c. eat more seaweed.
   d. stock the oceans.
3. In order to change seawater to fresh water, it must first be
   a. changed to steam and cooled.
   b. cooled to 32°F and filtered.
   c. placed in special aluminum containers.
   d. treated with chlorine.

II. EXPLANATION, PLEASE.

1. How do modern fishing methods differ from older ones?
2. What methods can be used to protect our fish stocks?
3. What are some requirements for setting up a sea farm?
4. Why are oceans considered to be "chemical gold mines"?

III. MATCH THE WORDS IN COLUMN A WITH THOSE IN COLUMN B. WRITE ONLY IN YOUR NOTEBOOK.

A	B
1. Process to change salt water to fresh water	a. Condensation
2. Method helpful in farming the sea	b. Tagging
3. Result of grinding up trash fish	c. Concentrated protein
4. Self-contained underwater living	d. Tektite I
5. Menhaden	e. Desalination
6. Changing steam to water	f. Mariculture
7. Oil	g. Habitats
	h. Trash fish
	i. Codfish
	j. Offshore rig

Projects for the Amateur Oceanographer

Tow line

Screw eye

Rubber or cork stopper

Line, taped or tied around neck

Narrow necked bottle

Metal weight

MAKE A WATER SAMPLING BOTTLE (*See Chapter 2*)

Professional oceanographers spend hundreds of dollars for the sampling bottles which can collect small quantities of water from various water depths. As an amateur oceanographer, you can make a device that will do a similar job for only pennies.

You will need a narrow-necked bottle such as a soda bottle. Find a cork or rubber stopper that will fit into the bottle. Attach a screw eye to the stopper. Mark off a tow-line in units of length. Use meters, fathoms, or feet, whichever you prefer. Thread the tow-line through the screw eye, and tie it securely. Leave about 18 inches hanging free. The bottle should be closed before it is dropped into the water.

Since it is filled with air, the bottle is too light to sink to the desired depth. Therefore, you will need to weight the bottle with fishing sinkers or scrap metal to make it heavy enough to sink. Use waterproof glue to keep the metal or sinkers in place on the bottom of the bottle. The extra length of line is used to attach the stopper to the neck of the bottle.

To use the sampling bottle, first put the stopper in place. Lower the bottle to the depth you wish. Then, jerk the tow-line to pull the stopper from the bottle. Water will now rush into the bottle. The line is firmly attached to the neck of the bottle, so all you have to do is pull gently to raise the bottle. Since you used a narrow-necked bottle, there will be very little exchange of water as you bring up the sample.

You can use this water sample to determine the salt content or temperature of the water at various levels. You can check the color of the water and even test it for various chemicals and animal life.

A VIEWING PORT: YOUR WINDOW TO THE SEA
(*See Chapter 3*)

Oceanographers, as you have learned, have developed a whole family of underwater vehicles to take them on discovery trips into the sea. The amateur oceanographer can make discoveries with the aid of a viewing port which will make it possible to see under water without getting wet.

You can construct a viewing tunnel about 18 inches long made of wood. The viewing area should be about 4 inches high and about 8 inches wide. Nail all parts together tightly because the tunnel must not leak. Press some putty or caulking compound into the seams to make them waterproof. To do away with reflections, paint the inside of the tunnel with flat, black paint. Mount a piece of glass across one end of the tunnel, and seal it in place with small nails, strips of wooden moulding, and putty.

Place the glass window into the water and bring your face close to the open end. You will now be able to watch fish and other underwater creatures in their own habitat. A viewing port is truly a window to the sea.

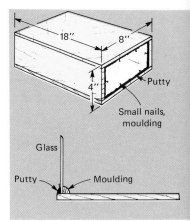

HOW TO MAKE AN OCEANOGRAPHER'S
BUCKET THERMOMETER (*See Chapter 10*)

A knowledge of water temperature is extremely important to the working oceanographer. An interesting project for the amateur might be to take the temperature of a nearby lake or ocean and to compare those readings with the daily changes in air temperature.

It is very easy to get an accurate measurement of air temperature. Simply hold up the thermometer and read the temperature. It is not as easy to get the water's temperature. If we were to attach a string to a thermometer and lower it into the ocean, the wet thermometer would be exposed to the wind before we could read the temperature. The wind would cause the thermometer to cool down and give us a very low, incorrect reading. To solve this problem, we can mount the thermometer inside of a plastic bottle. Lower the bottle. Pull it up after it fills with water. Then read the temperature. Since the thermometer is protected from the wind, and it is still surrounded by water, this method gives a very accurate reading.

It is even more convenient to use such a device if a large window is cut out of the front of the bottle. The bottom of the bottle acts as a bucket to hold the water around the bulb of the thermometer.

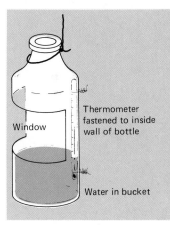

Oceanography Dictionary

The words listed here are key words to understanding oceanography. For other important words, see the INDEX.

abiotic	AY-by-ot-ik	Nonliving factors in the environment.
abyss	uh-BIS	Deepest parts of the ocean.
algae	AL-jee	Simple green plants lacking roots, stems or leaves.
atolls	A-tuhlz	Coral reef growth on top of a submerged mountain or volcano.
basalt	buh-SALT	Rock formed when the lava of ancient volcanoes cooled rapidly.
basin	BAY-sin	The bottom of the ocean floor.
biodegradable	BY-o-dee-GRAY-duh-bul	Capable of being decomposed by bacteria into simple substances.
biome	BY-ome	Large ecosystems throughout the world (desert, grasslands, woodlands, etc.).
biosphere	BY-uh-sfeer	Parts of the world which support life. Made up of living things and nonliving environment.
biotic	by-OT-ik	Relating to life—biological.
breakers		Large waves which release their energy on the shore.
continental shelf	kon-tuh-NEN-tul	The part of the ocean floor which extends from the shore to a depth of 600 feet.
continental slope		The part of the ocean floor which extends from the shelf to the deep ocean.
continents		Large masses of land on earth.
convection currents	kon-VEK-shun	The transfer of heat through liquids.
coral	KAR-ul	Skeleton remains left by reef-building animals.
crest	KREST	The top of a wave.
crust		Outermost section of the solid portion of the earth.

currents		Moving body of water.
desalination	dee-sal-uh-NAY-shun	The process of removing salt from sea water.
diatom	DY-uh-tum	Single-celled plants enclosed in a shell made up of silica.
dune area		A hill or ridge of sand piled up by the wind.
ebb		Water level or tide at its low point.
echo sounding		A method of finding the ocean's depths by sending out sound waves.
ecology	ee-KOL-uh-jee	Study of organisms, their relationships to each other and their environment.
ecosystem		Includes the living community and non-living factors which support it (sunlight, chemicals, water).
erosion	ee-RO-zhun	The wearing away of land as water flows over it.
estuary	ES-chuh-wair-ee	Brackish body of water formed from a drowned river valley. Its mouth opens to the sea.
flood		Tide level at its highest point.
fossil	FOS-ul	Remains of animals and plants which lived many ages ago.
fringing reef		A reef which develops close to the shore and has a shallow channel between it and the shore.
gullies	GUL-eez	Miniature valleys formed by running water.
gyres	JY-urz	A circular movement of water; e.g. major currents float around hemispheres in circular patterns.
habitat	HAB-uh-tat	A place in the environment where an organism lives.
hydrologic	hy-druh-LOJ-ik	Referring to the earth's water cycle.
hydrometer	hy-DROM-uh-tur	Instrument used to measure salinity and density of seawater.
hydrosphere	HY-druh-sfeer	Part of the earth covered by water.
intertidal		Area of the sea which is covered and uncovered by tides.
islands		Bodies of land surrounded by water; smaller than a continent.
lagoon	luh-GOON	A small bay located in the center of an atoll.

mariculture	MAH-ri-kul-chur	The method of growing plants and animals in sea water.
marine biology		The study of the life of the sea.
Nansen bottle	NAN-sun	Instrument used to collect water samples.
navigators	NAV-uh-gay-turz	Persons trained to find the position and direction of ships or airplanes.
neap tides	NEEP	Low tides when the moon and sun are at right angles to one another.
nodules	NOD-yoolz	Raised mounds on the sea floor made up of manganese.
oceanographers	o-shu-NOG-ruh-furz	Scientists who study the oceans.
offshore bar		Formed from sand being carried out to sea and deposited.
phases	FAY-ziz	Different views of the moon caused by differences in positions of earth and moon.
phytoplankton	fy-to-PLANK-tun	Group of plant plankton.
reefs		Coral formation built near the shore.
rip current		A movement of water from the shore line out to sea again.
salinity	suh-LIN-uh-tee	The amount of dissolved minerals in seawater.
scuba	SKOO-buh	*Self Contained Underwater Breathing Apparatus.* Permits diver to swim underwater without a connection to the surface.
spawning		Reproductive process of fish.
spring tides		Very high and low tides due to sun and moon being in a direct line.
strand line		Debris washed up on the beach; made up of dead sea weeds, driftwood and man-made articles.
submarine canyons		A steep valley cut out of the continental shelf and slope.
submergent	sub-MUR-junt	Shoreline having many bays and inlets. Resulted from a rise in the sea level which caused land valleys to become flooded.
substrate	SUB-strayt	Surface where an organism lives.
thermal	THUR-mul	Heated water which results from the cooling of electrical generators.
thermocline	THUR-mo-kline	Region between warm and cold areas in water.

178

tidal bore		Results from narrow channel changing shape of incoming tide. Water has a steep front as it travels upstream.
tidal creeks		Small creeks which divide marshes into little islands.
tidal range		The distance a tide travels between its low and high points.
tide pools		Pools formed on the shore by the outgoing tide.
tides		Movement of seawater caused by pull of the sun and the moon.
topography	tuh-POG-ruh-fee	The study of the shape of the earth's surface including its mountains, valleys, streams and lakes.
trade winds		Powerful winds in tropical regions, the major driving forces of currents in these areas.
trenches		Deep places in the ocean floor.
trough	TRAWF	Low point of a wave.
tsunami	tsoo-NOM-ee	Giant waves caused by disturbance on the ocean floor.
turbidity currents	tur-BID-uh-tee	Great undersea currents of silt and sand.
undertow		Strong current which heads out to sea where incoming waves are weaker.
vertebrae	VUR-tuh-bray	Bones making up the backbone of higher animals.
wave-cut cliff		Cliffs resulting from action of waves against rocky shoreline.
wave-cut terrace		Results from rocks accumulating at the base of the cliff.
wetlands		Another word used to describe salt marshes.
whitecaps		Powerful wind-driven waves which start breaking before they reach the shore.
zonation		Results from a population of organisms living in a certain area.
zooplankton	zo-uh-PLANK-tun	Animal plankton, includes copepods and one-celled animals.

Index

Acknowledgments

The photographs included in this text, on the pages indicated below, appear courtesy of the following:

American Cetacean Society, 144-1

American Museum of Natural History, 125-1, 125-2, 127-1 (bottom), 134-2

Ancona, George, 4-1

Arcadia National Park, 47-2, 50-2, 95-1, 103-1, 103-2, 103-3

Australia News and Information Service, 89 (bottom right), 126-1, 126-2

Canadian Government Travel Bureau, 77-2

Center for Media Development, Inc., 11-1A, 13-1, 13-2, 15-2, 22-1, 46-1, 89 (top left, top right, and bottom left), 102-2, 107-1, 116-1, 128-1B, 131-1, 131-3, 132-2, 133-1, 133-2, 138-1, 148-2, 154-1, 159-1, 169-1, 169-2

College of Mount St. Vincent on-Hudson 10-1 (Bob Eckman)

Consulate General of Japan, New York, 170-1

Coronet Instructional Media, 15-1, 27-1, 108-1, 109, 125-3, 127-1 (top)

Environmental Protection Administration, 162-1A, 162-1B, 162-2

Florida Department of Natural Resources, 148-2

Florida State News Bureau, Talahassee, 124-2

Goldfeld, Burton I., 83-1, 102-1, 155-1

Grumman Aerospace Corporation, 25-1

Hults, Walter, 89 (center)

Inmont Corporation/Long Island Oyster Farms, 171-1

Israeli Ministry of Tourism, 84-1

Japanese National Tourist Organization, 134-1, 117-2

Kelco Co., San Diego, California, 119-1

Kirouac, Paul J., viii, 65-1

Kitchen, H.W., 24-1, 51-2, 52-1, 68-1, 172-2

Marineland of Florida, St. Augustine, Florida, 140-1, 148-1

NASA, 20-1, 168-2 (bottom)

National Marine Fisheries Services, 59-2 (Gareth W. Coffin), 94-1, 141-2

National Oceanographic and Atmospheric Administration, 70-1, 70-2

New York Ocean Science Laboratory, 21-1, 118-1 (top), 146-1

New York Public Library, 3-1, 3-2 (bottom), 90-2

New York Times, 55-1, 75-1

Norwegian Information Center, 62-1

Scripps Institute of Oceanography, University of California, San Diego, 25-2, 29-1

Standard Oil Company of New Jersey, 40-2 (top), 40-2 (bottom)

The Port Authority of New York, 151-1

United States Army Corps of Engineers, 47-1, 51-1

United States Coast Guard, Seattle Washington, 49-1, 56-1 (Lt. Commander Charles W. Morgan)

United States Department of the Interior, 139-1, 164-1 (Roger Dexter), 165-1, 170-2

United States Department of the Navy, Naval Research Center, 90-1

United States Forest Service, 150-1, 152-1

United States Naval Oceanographic Office, 3-2 (top)

United States Naval Photographic Center, 19-1, 23-1, 33-1, 43-1, 147-1, 168-1

Ward's Natural Science Establishment, 83-2, 93-2, 118-1 (bottom), 132-1

Woods Hole Oceanographic Institute, 11-1B, 110-1